TEACHING AND LEARNING
ADOLESCENT PSYCHIATRY

THE PROCEEDINGS OF THE CONFERENCE ON TRAINING IN ADOLESCENT PSYCHIATRY

Sponsored by

The American Society for Adolescent Psychiatry

and

The Student Mental Health Clinic of the University of Chicago

Supported by a grant from the Charlotte Rosenbaum Fund through the auspices of John F. Kramer

Daniel Offer, M.D., *Chairman*

TEACHING AND LEARNING ADOLESCENT PSYCHIATRY

Edited by

DANIEL OFFER, M.D.

*Michael Reese Hospital
University of Chicago
Chicago, Illinois*

and

JAMES F. MASTERSON, M.D.

*New York Hospital (Payne Whitney Clinic)
Cornell University Medical College
New York, New York*

C H A R L E S   C   T H O M A S   •   P U B L I S H E R
Springfield   •   Illinois   •   U.S.A.

Published and Distributed Throughout the World by

CHARLES C THOMAS • PUBLISHER

BANNERSTONE HOUSE

301-327 East Lawrence Avenue, Springfield, Illinois, U.S.A.

NATCHEZ PLANTATION HOUSE

735 North Atlantic Boulevard, Fort Lauderdale, Florida, U.S.A.

With THOMAS BOOKS *careful attention is given to all details of
manufacturing and design. It is the Publisher's desire to present books
that are satisfactory as to their physical qualities and artistic possibilities
and appropriate for their particular use.* THOMAS BOOKS *will be true
to those laws of quality that assure a good name and good will.*

Printed in the United States of America

CC-11

PARTICIPANTS AND CONTRIBUTORS

Robert L. Arnstein, M.D.

Chief Psychiatrist
Department of University Health
Associate Clinical Professor in Psychiatry
Yale University
New Haven, Connecticut

Paul R. Dommermuth, Ph.D.

Associate Professor of Sociology
State University of New York
Fredonia, New York

Sherman C. Feinstein, M.D.

President, American Society for Adolescent Psychiatry
Director, Child and Adolescent Training Program
Institute for Psychosomatic and Psychiatric Research and Training
Michael Reese Hospital
Chicago, Illinois

Daniel X. Freedman, M.D.

Professor and Chairman
Department of Psychiatry
University of Chicago
Chicago, Illinois

Ghislaine D. Godenne, M.D.

Associate Professor of Psychiatry
The Johns Hopkins University
Baltimore, Maryland

Robert E. Gould, M.D.

Director, Adolescent Services
Bellevue Psychiatric Hospital
Associate Professor of Psychitary
University Medical Center
New York, New York

Roy R. Grinker, Sr., M.D.

Director, Institute for Psychosomatic and Psychiatric
Research and Training
Michael Reese Hospital
Chicago, Illinois

Willard J. Hendrickson, M.D.

Chief of Adolescent Service
Associate Professor of Psychiatry
University of Michigan
Ann Arbor, Michigan

Harold Hodgkinson, Ph.D.

Project Director
Center for Research and Development in Higher Education
University of California
Berkeley, California

Merton J. Kahne, M.D.

Psychiatrist-In-Chief, and Professor of Social Psychiatry
Massachusetts Institute of Technology
Cambridge, Massachusetts

John F. Kramer, M.D.

Associate Professor of Psychiatry
Chief, Student Mental Health Clinic
University of Chicago
Chicago, Illinois

Edwin Z. Levy, M.D.

Staff Psychiatrist, Children's Hospital
The Menninger Foundation
Faculty, Menninger School of Psychiatry
Topeka, Kansas

James F. Masterson, M.D.

Clinical Professor of Psychiatry
Cornell University Medical College
Head Adolescent Program
New York Hospital (Payne Whitney Psychiatric Clinic)
New York, New York

Salvador Minuchin, M.D.

Professor of Child Psychiatry
University of Pennsylvania
Philadelphia, Pennsylvania

Daniel Offer, M.D.

Associate Director, Institute for Psychosomatic and Psychiatric
Research and Training
Michael Reese Hospital
Associate Professor of Psychiatry
University of Chicago
Chicago, Illinois

J. P. Plunkett, M.D.

Director of Training and Clinical Services
Division of Student Mental Health
Associate Clinical Professor of Psychiatry
Yale University
New Haven, Connecticut

Donald B. Rinsley, M.D.

Chief, Adolescent Unit, Children's Service
Topeka State Hospital
Faculty, Menninger School of Psychiatry
Associate Clinical Professor of Psychiatry
University of Kansas School of Medicine
Kansas City, Kansas

William A. Schonfeld, M.D.

*Immediate Past President, American Society for Adolescent Psychiatry
Assistant Clinical Professor of Child Psychiatry
Columbia University
New York, New York*

Bertram Slaff, M.D.

*President Elect, American Society for Adolescent Psychiatry
Associate Clinical Professor of Adolescent Psychiatry
Mount Sinai School of Medicine
New York, New York*

Frank S. Williams, M.D.

*Director, Julia Ann Singer Preschool Psychiatric Center,
Senior Staff Psychiatrist, Department of Child Psychiatry
Divisions of Psychiatry
Cedars-Sinai Medical Center
Los Angeles, California*

INTRODUCTION

T HIS BOOK REPORTS a conference which not only crowned fifteen years of growth in adolescent psychiatry, but also served as an opportunity to consolidate and integrate what had been learned, and to probe the training needs of the future.

The last fifteen years have witnessed the extraordinary growth of adolescent psychiatry in response to the challenge presented by adolescents' need for care. There has been a great increase in the percentage of adolescents seen by mental health workers; 25 percent of all persons served by psychiatric outpatient clinics in the United States are between the ages of ten and nineteen.[1] By 1975 it is estimated that one-half of the population will be under twenty-five, compared to 40 percent in 1960.[2]

In addition, in our culture, unlike some old-world cultures, such a premium is placed upon independence and individuality that American adolescents are much more outspoken in their demand for care. For example, recently at the Michael Reese Hospital in Chicago, three ghetto teenagers stalked into the outpatient clinic demanding psychiatric treatment. The Illinois legislature has recently passed a bill giving teenagers permission to obtain treatment for venereal disease without the permission or knowledge of their parents. In Georgia, the governor has just signed into law a provision that teenagers may get psychotherapy without the permission of their parents.

The extraordinary increase in numbers combined with the adolescent's independence, readiness and right to demand care created a need which psychiatry in the early 1950's was ill-equipped to meet. For example, at that time the. Institute of Juvenile Research in Chicago, a state supported child guidance clinic, accepted children only up to the age of fifteen. The University of Illinois Clinic on the other hand admitted patients only after the age of eighteen had been reached. Those between fifteen and eighteen were left in a therapeutic vacuum.

The adolescent in the 1950's became the stepchild of psychiatry. Most outpatients were treated in children's clinics, not adolescents' clinics. There were few, if any, inpatient services for adolescents (psychiatrists were terrified that adolescents would wreck their institutions, since few techniques for control were known). There was no integrated psychoanalytic theory of adolescent development; little was written on psychotherapy, except by Aichorn, Bernfeld, A. Freud and a few others; and there was little clinical research.

In the last fifteen years the situation has changed drastically. The efforts of workers in the field, many of whom have contributed to this volume, have produced a remarkable "knowledge explosion." Adolescents are now generally referred to adolescent outpatient clinics, not child guidance clinics. Adolescent inpatient services are springing up across the land. A comprehensive integrated psychoanalytic theory of personality development has been described. Clinical psychiatric study of the problems of adolescence has burgeoned. (See Basic Reading List in Appendix.)

The organizational counterpart to these developments has been the American Society for Adolescent Psychiatry, which has grown from local to national proportions, and is the sponsor of this meeting.

Perhaps the joint experience of the editors typifies and symbolizes the events of these years. We both entered the field in the 1950's, began research projects, and worked to establish training programs and organizations to foster the development of knowledge about adolescence. The paralleling of our research interests caused us to meet, a meeting which has borne fruit for both of us in the collaboration on this volume.

Probably the most significant of all these developments is that so many people—psychoanalysts, psychiatrists, psychologists, social workers and others—now have had fifteen years of learning and seasoning which have prepared them to expand knowledge further as well as to train others.

Clearly the time was ripe for this conference, a moment of pause to evaluate where we stand and where we are going.

A number of issues have contributed to the confusion in current thinking about adolescence. First, the view that adolescence is an in-between stage (part child, part adult) has often led child psychiatrists to focus on the child and the adult psychiatrist to focus on the adult. Second, attempting to place adolescence within certain age limits has similarly led to confusion. Third, the old argument about how much of adolescence is due to cultural, and how much to biological, forces has contributed confusions of its own. Although cultural forces shape the form which adolescence takes, our specific interest as psychiatrists is in the normal and pathological aspects of emotional development. Adolescence, from this point of view, should not be considered just an in-between stage but as a stage in its own right with its own unique developmental or growth tasks. It begins with puberty and extends until the essential emotional developmental tasks have been achieved, no matter what the age. These tasks have been variously defined, for example: (a) emancipation from the parents, (b) the achievement of a sense of identity, and (c) the capacity for heterosexual intimacy.

The impact of economic and cultural forces in the United States, with increasing specialization and industrialization, so prolong adolescence that in all probability these growth tasks are not fully achieved until the end of the college years. For this reason we have included work with college students in this volume. Though clearly the college and high school experience differ, they are at the same time only phases of the same growth process.

This book, divided into six sections, aproaches the theme of training from the traditional as well as from the social psychiatric point of view.

The first section, entitled "The Process," presents a single paper by one of the editors, Dr. James F. Masterson, which takes a somewhat philosophical look at the process of teaching and learning psychotherapy with adolescents. It deals with such questions as: What are the motivations of the teacher doing this work?; What are the satisfactions?; What obstacles does he encounter?, and, What are the prices he must pay? From the point of view of the student it deals with the following: What is he expected to learn?; What are the pitfalls he encounters in learning?, and, How does learning relate to his own emotional development?

The second section, entitled "The Programs," is comprised of four papers which describe actual programs from two different points of view. The first two reflect the older, more traditional emphasis on the individual, one-to-one, dyadic relationship as the core of the training experience. The latter two reflect the more recent emphasis on community or social-psychiatric approaches.

The first paper by Dr. Willard Hendrickson, describing his training program at the University of Michigan, reflects the point of view that first priority in training must be given to closely supervised, direct, concentrated, clinical experience with a relatively few inpatients where the resident can learn from direct observation of a patient's reenactment of past neurotic conflicts in relation to himself, as well as to other members of the staff. Dr. Hendrickson also stresses the importance of the resident performing numerous parentlike functions such as advising, demanding, disciplining, teaching, prohibiting, etc., thereby learning how to integrate in his therapy both administrative and psychotherapeutic approaches.

The second paper in this section, by Doctors Arnstein and Plunkett, provides an elaborate description of the training program for residents in Mental Health Psychiatry at Yale University, and it also briefly reviews the history of the development of college psychiatry. The training program for third and fourth year fellows revolves around a core of clinical work, including initial evaluation, individual psychotherapy, group therapy, supervision and emergency coverage.

Doctors Arnstein and Plunkett make the point that experience at a college differs from ordinary psychoanalytically oriented psychotherapy in the following ways: The college experience is an important aspect of human development, consequently a small amount of therapy will often allow the individual to continue his natural development. This leads to the acceptance of minor shifts in goals which allow the developmental thrust to continue. The fact that the student is living away from home makes him more independent in that he has the opportunity to seek treatment on his own without the knowledge of his parents. Since being in college is a desirable state of affairs for the student's development, considerable effort is made to provide supportive therapy simply to prolong that state. Consequently, therapeutic attention gets focused at times on the very short range goals of resolving emotional conflicts interfering with academic progress.

Doctor Gould and Doctor Kahne describe training programs which focus on the community as well as on the individual. Though their respective settings are at opposite ends of the spectrum, the former in a large city hospital within a ghetto environment and the latter on a college campus, both emphasize the importance of the transactions of the patient in his natural habitat. They maintain that past emphasis on diagnosis, evaluation, disposition and therapy of the individual patient is not enough. They stress a field or system approach where the individual can be understood best, not only as an independent organism, but also in continuous interaction with his environment.

Doctor Gould points out that, though one-to-one therapy is by no means obsolete for today's training programs, the psychiatrist has to develop ever so much more complex skills in administration and consultation, and an ability to transmit his skills to paramedical and parapsychiatric personnel.

Doctor Kahne's program at Massachusetts Institute of Technology does not focus on students alone; rather, it is moving towards becoming a community psychiatric resource. Doctor Kahne and his colleagues are available to faculty, administration, personnel and workers at all levels and their friends and families on the campus. In such a way, Doctor Kahne is able to maintain what he views as a true social-psychiatric program. He not only treats the individual students for their problems; rather he is a psychiatric consultant for the entire campus.

The third section, entitled "Family Therapy: One Type of Intervention," illustrates one specific mode of treatment. Since we recognize that it is not possible to include adequate consideration of all the various parameters of work with adolescents such as delinquency, drugs, etc., we selected the following point of view to be presented in more detail.

Doctor Minuchin emphasizes that techniques of intervention have been limited by the fact that most of the major theoretical systems have been concerned only with the influence of both internal and external factors in the development of the child. He presents and illustrates with one detailed case the ecological point of view that three elements must be studied independently: (a) the child as an individual, (b) the environment in which the behavior is observed, and (c) the linkage between these two elements. The therapist operating within an ecological framework can study his patient in different contexts determining the significance of those contexts and their relationship to each other. Then he can determine where and how intervention will be maximally effective. The child's family will usually be the most significant area for intervention, although the schools, peers, neighborhood or others may sometimes be significant.

The fourth section, entitled "Sociological Perspectives," presents adolescent psychiatry as seen by two sociologists. In the first paper, Dr. Hodgkinson presents his view of the college psychiatrist's function, which has recently come under attack due to a purported split in the psychiatrist's allegiance to patient versus college. Doctor Hodgkinson sees this split allegiance as an asset and encourages the psychiatrist to place more emphasis in his work on how institutional factors produce pathology. He suggests that the skills and perceptions of the psychiatrist are much too precious to be reserved for the consultation room alone, and that he should consider a new role moving across the strata of academic faculty, student and administrative personnel providing emotional feedback to administrators and encouraging trust and getting people to talk honestly to each other. Thus Doctor Hodgkinson emphasizes and widens further Doctor Gould's and Doctor Kahne's purpose to extend training to community areas.

The coalescence of a professional group devoted to adolescent psychiatry is of recent origin. The American Society for Adolescent Psychiatry was founded in 1967 under the presidency of William A. Schonfeld. There are many different views on the role of such a society in the professionalization of a particular field and/or its members. Doctor Dommermuth has been studying with Dr. Rue Bucher the social processes involved in young physicians becoming psychiatrists. He was present at our conference, circulated questionnaires and obtained interviews with some of the leaders of the American Society for Adolescent Psychiatry. In his paper he presents the data he has collected about adolescent psychiatry as an emerging field.

The fifth section, entitled "A Summing Up," highlights some of the problems raised in our conference. We were fortunate in having with us the perception and wisdom of an experienced clinician and investigator, Doctor Roy Grinker, Sr. He read all the papers in advance and also attended the entire conference. In giving his evaluation he raises many cogent questions and returns to the consistent theme that we must subject our theories and our practice to careful and methodical study.

The council of the American Society for Adolescent Psychiatry after much deliberation was able to produce an official position statement on training which helped to condense and clarify the many issues raised by the conference. It should be of great interest to all those seeking answers to these questions. It has been placed in the Appendix at the end of the formal papers where it is readily available for reference.

The editors have also included in the Appendix a Basic Reading List on Adolescence for those interested.

REFERENCES

1. Rosen, B. M.; Bahn, A. K.; Shellow, R., and Bower, F. M.: Adolescent patients served in outpatient psychiatric clinics. *Amer J Public Health, 55*:1563–1577, 1965.
2. United States Census, 1960.

ACKNOWLEDGMENTS

The organization of this conference, which took place at the Center for Continuing Education of the University of Chicago, November 14–15, 1969, was the responsibility of a Committee on Training of the American Society for Adolescent Psychiatry (listed below), appointed by Dr. William A. Schonfeld, then President, and assisted by Dr. Sherman C. Feinstein, the President elect.

THE COMMITTEE ON TRAINING

Chairman: Dr. D. Offer

Members: Dr. A. D. Copeland
Dr. S. C. Feinstein
Dr. G. D. Godenne
Dr. R. E. Gould
Dr. W. J. Hendrickson
Dr. J. F. Kramer
Dr. J. F. Masterson
Dr. B. R. Slaff
Dr. R. A. Solow
Dr. H. Warner
Dr. F. S. Williams
Dr. H. H. Work

Dr. Daniel X. Freedman, Chairman of the Department of Psychiatry at the University of Chicago, and Dr. Roy R. Grinker, Sr., Chairman of the Department of Psychiatry at the Michael Reese Hospital and Medical Center, gave the conference their complete support. The conference was underwritten by a grant from the Charlotte Rosenbaum Fund to the Student Mental Health Clinic of the University of Chicago. Dr. John F. Kramer, the chief of this clinic, was instrumental in making this fund available and helped in many

xviii Teaching and Learning Adolescent Psychiatry

more ways than it is possible to mention to make the conference a success.

Finally, we would like to express our deep thanks to Miss Helen Goodell for her efficient assistance in organizing, editing and indexing the book, to Nancy A. Scanlan for providing peerless secretarial services and to Raye Korshak and Judith Offer, our proofreaders.

DANIEL OFFER
JAMES F. MASTERSON

CONTENTS

TEACHING AND LEARNING
ADOLESCENT PSYCHIATRY

Section I

THE PROCESS

Chapter One

To Teach Is to Learn Twice: Teaching and Learning the Art of Psychotherapy with Adolescents

JAMES F. MASTERSON

> I had to grow old to learn what I wanted
> to know, and I should need to be young
> to say well what I know. To teach is to
> learn twice!
>
> *Pensées* (1842)
> JOSEPH JOUBERT

I HAVE LONG BEEN ATTRACTED to a good title for its own sake in the same way that some people are attracted to a painting or a piece of sculpture. For example, when I was suddenly asked for a title for this essay the above came to mind and I impulsively spelled it out as epitomizing my thesis: we must teach to learn, we must learn to teach. Imagine my shock and dismay many months later when I sat down to write and realized that I would have to come up with something that lived up to the title. Well, to be forewarned is to be forearmed and I hope in this case to be disarmed.

So now in writing about teaching and learning the art of psychotherapy with adolescents I have neither reviewed the literature, nor done any surveys of special studies. Instead, I have tried to mine my own thin vein of personal experience to sift out those few nuggets that may be of some general usefulness in this very complex endeavor in which we are all engaged.

For some people life itself is not a sufficiently complex endeavor; they must complicate it further by taking on even

5

greater challenges. Prominent among these people are psychiatrists who have chosen not only to treat adolescents, but also to try to teach others to do the same. What follows are my own reflections on this incredibly challenging, frustrating but satisfying task.

THE LEARNING PROCESS

Learning as well as teaching the art of psychotherapy with adolescents takes place within the matrix of complicated emotional growth processes. The appropriate model, it seems to me, is not a supervisor teaching a resident, but a triad—three people—supervisor, resident and patient joined together temporarily in a common endeavor, each a teacher and each a student. The supervisor carries the ultimate responsibility, but all three both teach and learn.

The supervisor and the resident each bring to the common task on the one hand intellectual knowledge, and on the other, a more or less successful resolution of the unique emotional growth tasks of their own development. The supervisor has the most perspective and knowledge, and also he has most likely come further in resolving his own growth tasks, hopefully to the point of having chosen a "way of life"—a unique personality or character style. Even this chosen "way of life" must constantly be subjected to the reexamination that supervision of each new trainee, and indeed, the doing of therapy demand.

The resident, closer to his own adolescence, has far less knowledge. Fortunately, he is shielded from too much anxiety over this fact by his ignorance. In addition, not having fully resolved his own growth tasks, more than likely he has yet to choose a "way of life." The third member of the triad, the patient, in the midst of his adolescence, confronts anew the age-old problem of development. He has the least knowledge and the farthest to go. Yet he probably has the most potential for redirection and growth.

Each tosses his share into the common emotional pot, creating a veritable psychological bouillabaisse which simmers and boils until each emerges to go his own way. If the work has been sucessful none will be exactly the same again—for each will have changed both in knowledge and in progress towards resolution of his own growth tasks. Each will be both "wiser" and more "grown-up."

This learning process, much like psychotherapy, consists of three phases: engagement, involvement and separation. In the engagement phase, the supervisor must work with the resident's resistances every bit as much as the resident must work with the patient's. In the involvement phase a common bond develops between the three not unlike that shared by soldiers in combat. The last, or separation, phase, requiring the giving up of this bond, is probably the most difficult as it tests the degree of success of the entire enterprise.

I do not intend to examine this process simply from the point of view of cognition or learning. This aspect is itself quite complex, but I suspect that you are every bit as familiar with the issues as I am. Rather I propose briefly to discuss a well-known but much less talked about issue that has enmeshed my attention, i.e. how intellectual learning and the solving of emotional growth tasks go hand in hand for all three participants.

I shall concentrate first on the supervisor asking such questions as the following: What are his motivations for doing this work?; What is it about his personality that draws him into these hazardous waters?; What does the work offer him?; What are his satisfactions?; What obstacles does he encounter?, and, What are the prices he must pay? I shall spend less time on the resident to consider such questions as: What does he expect to learn?; What are some of the "traps" he encounters in learning?, and, How does learning relate to his own emotional development? I shall touch very briefly on some of the same issues in even less detail for the patient, since the focus of this paper is on teaching.

SUPERVISOR

The ordinary person, when he has resolved his growth tasks and grown up, or when he has simply gotten older—

whichever the case may be—is relieved and grateful to have the turbulent growth tasks and conflicts of adolescence settle into the bog of his memory of things past where they can remain submerged until his children's adolescence rears up to cause them to surface again for a further hearing.

If this is the usual course of events, then those of us who supervise pyschotherapy with adolescents must have taken another course. We do not turn our backs on our own adolescence, and thereby permit it to settle, but we have the temerity to think so highly of our own solutions to our growth tasks as to present them as models for others. In addition, figuratively speaking, we stick our noses into everybody else's adolescence. What effect does this have on us? Are we able to flaunt our own course with impunity, or is there some grievous price to pay?

It will be my thesis that this work of teaching others about adolescence actually promotes our adjustment by enabling us to reaffirm our "way of life" in our daily toil, thereby reinforcing the solutions we have made to our own unique developmental tasks. It is those solutions that have brought us to this supervisory work; it is this work that shores up and reinforces those solutions.

The supervisor's function on the social and professional level represents a form of expertise; on the personal emotional level it represents an end point to a long developmental pathway—a chosen way of life—the result of a unique set of choices from the many available to solve developmental tasks.

In my contacts with colleagues over the years I have been struck by the fact that those who do this work with adolescents seem to have a number of personality traits in common. Though they might differ quite dramatically in other respects, in these characteristics they seem to be quite similar. For example, consider such traits as the following: a commitment to the truth and to the facing of reality as indispensable in dealing with emotional conflicts; a disenchantment with prevailing cultural values; a vivid sense of the ironies and ambiguities of life with, nevertheless, a gusto about the potentialities of life; a quick and ready sense of humor, with a conviction about the frailty of human nature, a frailty, however, which often can be transcended. I suspect that these very characteristics are the sinews of this chosen "way of life."

The supervisor in the course of his development learned a great deal of objective information which when sifted through his developing personality resulted in his chosen professional interest. The choice was made not only in response to external stimuli, but also in response to how these stimuli aided or helped him to contain and resolve his own childhood conflicts and thereby solve his own growth tasks. Again, from the social point of view the supervisor is a learned expert, while from the individual's point of view the practice of his expertise represents the solution to the task of his own development. Thus his expertise represents both learned knowledge and a way of life, a viewpoint on clinical material as well as a point of view on life.

One could classify supervisors' personality styles along a spectrum which ranges from directive-organic at one end to individual-psychoanalytic at the other. A supervisor at the one end is group-oriented and emphasizes direction, support and environmental manipulation. He places his greatest faith in direction, control and intellectually arranged solutions. One from the opposite end of the personality spectrum is individually oriented and emphasizes analysis and understanding. He places his greatest faith in the individual's capacity to cope through insight.

Again I say, the supervisor's place on that spectrum represents both learned knowledge and a way of life.

It is the expression of his unique point of view in his daily function that enables the supervisor to reaffirm himself. One thinks here of a number of analogies from the least neurotic to the most: the writer who escapes from emotional deprivation in childhood by writing about the social deprivation of Negroes; the philosopher such as Rousseau, who escapes from childhood domination and intimidation through his philosophy that man is good by nature, but corrupted by civilization; the policeman who contains his own antisocial impulses by working to apprehend criminals; the priest who manages his own conflicts by working with the sinner. The examples, of course, are endless. The essential point is that the specific function, while socially useful, also serves the individual as a unique form of sublimation for his childhood conflicts and reinforces and stablizes his life adjustment.

The supervisor, astride the mainstream of the human developmental process, serves as a guardian of the healthy progress of that process.

He may be likened to a sculptor whose material is the growth process—with one hand he guides the developing adolescent's management of his growth problems, and with the other he works with the parents to produce the optimal developmental pathway for his adolescent patient—thereby shaping and influencing the growth process itself. In the course of this work he refashions this microcosm of a world closer to the one he values—expressing these values through his work but neither imposing them on or making value judgments of others.

It may well be a comment on our culture, and on maturity as it is achieved in the United States today, that one can better express these values in work with the young than with the mature.

What are the hazards of this work? What is the price the supervisor must pay? First, the way of life the supervisor has chosen has an inevitable by-product. The place he has found on the spectrum of styles of personalities represents the keystone to the arch of his own personality. He can no more question this keystone than the committed Catholic can question the existence of God, for this would require questioning the foundation of his whole adjustment. Therefore, he is unable to discuss in simple objective fashion—either in his life or in his clinical work—those issues that touch on this keystone. Though he tries to keep an open mind, his necessary emotional commitment to his way of life defeats him. His conviction about his views springs more from this emotional commitment than from objective truth.

This can often be seen in the clinical situation in discussions about the details of therapy. In order to illustrate I will exaggerate two views using the classification of D-O and I-P. For example, should a mother be told how to handle her adolescent, or should she be helped by interpretation to understand the conflicts that prevent her from doing what is necessary? The D-O would argue for telling the mother what to do, feeling that not to do so would be allowing her to wallow in helplessness. The I-P, relying on interpretation, would feel that his colleague's approach promoted dependency. Though the demands of the clinical situation may lie somewhere in between and may actually vacillate from one to the other over time, no amount of argument, persuasion or evidence seems to settle the differences. The discussion changes very subtly from a collaborative scientific inquiry bent on pursuing the truth, to an adversary proceeding whose object is to defend one's way of life. It is well for the supervisor to be aware of the keystone of his own way of life in order to understand such discussions. The fact that it is the proper business of the growing person, be he resident or patient, to challenge these views in order to find solutions appropriate to his own needs makes such discussions inevitable.

Second, the good supervisor keeps one foot in maturity and another in adolescence and hopefully never fully matures in the sense that his developmental pathways become permanently closed. He must be prepared to lay open his own adjustment to constant challenge and reevaluation, and to deal with the internal adjustments dictated by constant change. He may lose sleep and tranquility, but he will not lose touch. He may lose stability and certainty, but not flexibility.

Third, the supervisory process itself is emotionally wearing. The necessity for the supervisor to repeat these intensive, often combative, relationships year in and year out with new people may deplete his resources if he is not careful to renew them in his personal life. He may find himself getting too involved, or placing too much protective distance between himself and patient or resident to the detriment of all.

RESIDENT

The resident in this triad of supervisor-resident-patient on the one level is seeking knowledge, but on the other he has not yet solved his own growth tasks and is still looking for a final way of life.

What do we expect the resident to learn? At the heart of the matter, of course, he is to learn adolescent psychopathology and psychotherapy. But, beyond that, he should acquire a feel, an intuition, developed through experience, of the relationship of the observable aspects of an adolescent's pathology to what is "going on" in his emotions underneath, a comprehension of how all these fit together so that he can sense when one part is clearly missing and can then seek it himself, a capacity to integrate those perceptions in such a way that they will lead him to the appropriate therapeutic response—whether this be limit setting, direction, empathy, support or interpretation. We expect the resident neither to comply, nor to copy, but to cope—to draw upon the depths of his own personality within the overall therapeutic framework that we supply to develop his own unique therapeutic style.

One of the supervisor's greatest contributions is the plumbing of the resident's countertransference which blocks his learning every bit as much as resistance blocks the patient's progress.

I have always found useful in this regard the stressing of human frailties and problems (i.e. those of the supervisor, of the resident, of the nursing staff, as well as of the patient) as an essential part of the game. There is no more salutary learning experience for a young inexperienced resident struggling with and frightened by his own countertransference than to observe his supervisor becoming aware of and consciously trying to deal with *his* countertransference. This view is particularly well put in the following: *

---

* W. S. Gilbert, "Yeoman of the Guard."

When they're offered to the world in merry guise
Unpleasant truths are swallowed with a will,
For he who'd make his fellow creatures wise
Should always gild the philosophic pill!

In other words, I strive for an atmosphere in which there is a certain amount of fun rather than disapproval in discovering the how and why of the latest "goof" in the patient's care. Parallel to this must be the emphasis on human reason, subject as it is to endless emotional influence, as the ultimate reed upon which to rely for clarification and support. Once the resident has become aware of and mastered his countertransference, the psychotherapy and the resident's learning seem to proceed apace.

What are some of the "traps" the resident encounters in his learning? He may feel caught between his patient who is constantly tempting him to regress and his supervisor who seems to be expecting him to act on knowledge he does not possess. These divergent demands promote great anxiety and exaggerate feelings of helplessness which may cause him to forego the slow, time-consuming, painful struggle for growth and learning and settle for a simple imitation of his "master's" supposed omniscience. This is particularly true in psychotherapy where the student not only has an awesome amount to learn, but also has charge over and responsibility for the life of another human being, who is at the same time his partner in the learning process.

This tendency is further aggravated, I fear, by medical education which seems to place the highest premium on the wholesale ingestion of the largest number of essentially indigestible facts. The student's curiosity and ingenuity are allowed to rust, wither and atrophy, perhaps never to rise again even to the most provocative of challenges. I sometimes wonder if the whole American educational system isn't similarly at fault in overlooking the function of the teacher as described by Goethe: *

---

* Johann Wolfgang Von Goethe, "Elective Affinities," Book I, Chapter 7.

A teacher who can arouse a feeling for a single mood or action, for one single good poem, accomplishes more than he who fills our memory with rows on rows of natural objects, classified with name and form.

Unfortunately the indoctrination techniques fostered by American education change learning from an active, stimulating process—involving observation, hypothesis formulation, testing and revision—into a passive rote-memory one. The student rather than being an alert, curious, interacting, responsive partner becomes a passive satellite operating under the restraint of intellectual control rather than the freedom and spontaneity of an emotional response to the pleasure inherent in the learning process.

The student all too often becomes an eager accomplice of the system in promoting the demise of his own most precious possessions, i.e. his independent curiosity and imagination. Should he make this neurotic bargain subordinating his independent thinking to the ingestion of facts from his teacher, in order to relieve his feelings of helplessness—the bargain fails. He does not receive the omnipotence he fantasies that his teacher possesses, if the teacher is any good.

The teacher's effectiveness is not based on accumulation or ingestion of facts, though he also has accumulated many facts, but rather on the personal growth that occurs through independent thinking and learning. The teacher's real effectiveness is in an individual and unique style of perceiving, reacting to, and integrating the subject being studied. This latter, the only course which realistically contains the feelings of helplessness, may fatally and finally elude the student who, frightened by his feelings of helplessness, remains buried under this avalanche of facts. He becomes a pseudospecialist. He can glibly recite all the differential diagnoses, but he fails to see the person in his patient.

It is a wonder to behold in my continuous case seminar the passivity and docility with which the students initially wait to be "taught." Blind to their perceptual ineptitude they resent my not "telling them what to do." They feel

my job is to provide "objective facts" which they will in-
gest. However, there is hope, for a far greater wonder is
to see how quickly and well they learn once their resentment has been worked through, with what zest and gusto
they plunge into the active process of thinking, testing—
learning. And I must add, that by the end of the year they
usually have my back against the wall, challenging my most
precious nostrums and rationalizations.

It is a testimony to the strength and vitality of their innate
curiosity and capacity to learn that twenty years of oppressive
suffocation have failed to snuff it out entirely.

The supervisor must constantly be aware of the dangers
that rigidity and stratification of knowledge pose to residents.
He could do no better than to follow the advice given many
years ago by Alexander Pope* in the following lines:

> The bookfull blockhead ignorantly read,
> With loads of learned lumber in his head,
> With his own tongue still edifies his ears,
> And always list'ning to himself appears.
> All books he reads, and all he reads assails
> For fools rush in where angels fear to tread.
> But where's the man who counsel can bestow,
> Still pleas'd to teach, and yet not proud to know?
> Careless of censure, nor too fond of fame,
> Still pleas'd to praise, yet not afraid to blame,
> Averse alike to flatter or offend,
> Not free from faults, nor yet too vain to mend.

How does this learning relate to the resident's search for
a way of life? The resident unconsciously identifies with his
therapist's various attitudes both towards clinical material
and towards life. These identifications serve as integral building
blocks to complete his own development and aid him in finding
his way of life. Ordinarily he rejects those attitudes that do
not "fit" his personality. If he settles for imitation again he
may well end up with building blocks totally unsuitable to the
structure underneath. Should he have a supervisor whose

---

* Alexander Pope, "An Essay on Criticism."

functioning represents an extremely neurotic rather than a constructive solution to developmental tasks, he runs risks both at the level of knowledge as well as at the level of building blocks for growth and development.

It is the wise and perceptive resident who is able to test out the degree to which the views of his supervisor represent objective clinical truth and/or his way of life. Often the resident may perceive his supervisor's need to use denial. If the supervisor can accept the resident's confrontation he may learn as much from the resident as the resident learns from him.

PATIENT

Now we come to the third and most significant member of the triad—the patient. Despite the fact that he has the least knowledge and the most difficulty in solving his developmental tasks, his conflicts form the battleground upon which the entire endeavor takes place and he can be the greatest beneficiary of the outcome. Though he seeks primarily relief from suffering, if his treatment is successful he will achieve as by-products both learning and maturation.

As they fight for him, he challenges and assaults his resident's and his supervisor's personality structures both in reworking his childhood conflicts and in his resistance to therapeutic progress. In the beginning he may be the most deceptive and the least perceptive member of the triad, but within a surprisingly short period of time he can become not only the most open and direct but also the most perceptive member. Since the conflicts are immediate and intense to him, he can perceive their prototypes in his resident, in his supervisor, or in the institution long before they themselves are aware of his perceptions. While initially concealing these perceptions, as trust develops he will throw them into the common pool where they may possibly serve as stimuli for further development for all three.

CONCLUSION

In the last analysis the rewards of being a supervisor far

outweigh the handicaps, since one of life's greatest gifts is to have a socially useful, personally satisfying function which reinforces the solutions one has made to one's own growth tasks. The supervisor also receives the additional dividend of being both a participant in and a witness to one of nature's ever-recurring wonders—a resident's slow growth and development towards becoming a true professional.

I have tried to present a point of view on this triadic experience, realizing that not only is much left unsaid, but also that chips from the keystone of my own personality—sprinkled throughout the paper—have played a part in the consideration. I trust, however, that they are not so numerous as to change a scientific inquiry into a lawyer's brief.

At the conclusion of most presentations of this sort I tend to feel some disappointment and frustration. I didn't say what I dreamed but at least I did say what I could. My hope is that this essay will be for you what it has been for me—a stimulus for personal learning as well as for emotional growth.

Section II

THE PROGRAMS

Chapter Two

Training in Adolescent Psychiatry:
The Role of Experience with Inpatients

WILLARD J. HENDRICKSON

SEVERAL YEARS AGO I heard a most interesting "testimonial" from the wife of a resident. He had just completed an eight-month rotation on our adolescent service during which his work had rapidly improved to an excellent level, despite the really painful anxiety he experienced over it. Her comment to me was, "He went through hell when he was working with those kids, and so did I; but he ended up doing a lot of growing up. You should know that I once hated you and his patients for what you were doing to him, but now, I must confess, I appreciate it."

Although this wife's observation is a fairly typical one, my comments on some aspects of the teaching value of work with adolescent inpatients will, of course, not be based primarily on the testimony of residents' wives. Since they will be based on and illustrated by our experience on the Adolescent Service of the University of Michigan, a very brief description of that service is in order.

THE SETTING

The adolescent service began its development about 1950 within the adult wards, where the plan was undertaken to admit increasingly larger numbers of adolescents while actively developing a treatment and activity program for them. This led to the opening of a twenty-two bed coeducational, semi-open, all-adolescent ward in 1956. Since that date, the service has existed as a separate division in the Department of Psychiatry with an active diagnostic and treatment service for adolescent outpatients, and an inpatient service which includes a full-time school and a full and demanding series of activities particularly designed for adolescents. This service is an entirely self-contained administrative unit with all personnel who work with the youngsters assigned full time to the adolescent service and responsible to its chief. The program has always been richly staffed with respect to all activities, including sufficient psychiatrists so that intensive individual and group psychotherapy is available to each patient to the full extent of his abilities to make use of it.

TRAINEES INVOLVED

1. General Psychiatry Residents.
2. Many of the Fellows in Child Psychiatry. Their time on the adolescent service occurs for the most part during the first two years of general psychiatric training—occasionally extending into the first few months of the two year fellowship in child psychiatry.
3. Fellows in Adolescent Psychiatry. For many years we have accepted for advanced training psychiatrists who have completed three or more years of residency and who wish an additional year or two of specialized work with adolescents. For the past four years this has been formalized in official Fellowships, one for the fourth and one for the fifth year. These are partially financed by a training grant from NIMH.

THE PROGRAM

All the above are involved in much the same intensively supervised inpatient and outpatient work. The term "resident" as used in this paper may refer to any of the above three groups. Out of the total of some eighty residents we have trained over the years, by far the largest of the above three groups would be the general psychiatry residents, and next in numbers the fellows in child psychiatry. For all trainees, first priority is given to closely supervised, direct, concentrated clinical experience with a relatively few inpatients. It should be noted that in the case of fellows in adolescent psychiatry, additional emphasis is given to opportunities for administration, supervision and other teaching, research, and consultation in community agencies—all designed to prepare them for specialized work with adolescents, or to head up adolescent services elsewhere if they so desire.

Residents have been assigned full time to adolescent psychiatry for a minimum of eight months (regretfully sometimes reduced to six in recent years, due to pressures for them to spend time in new fields such as "community psychiatry"). We definitely favor this fulltime "total immersion" approach for an extended period, because of the complex and demanding nature of the work and of the learning tasks involved. We also strongly recommend, wherever possible, concurrent and closely integrated outpatient *and* inpatient experience. One sometimes hears the recommendation that since for better or for worse most of our residents leave training to make their living doing largely outpatient psychotherapy, the training should concentrate on outpatient experience. This concept seems particularly invalid in the case of adolescents. The resident may never learn what he has been missing in the way of overlooked or misinterpreted clinical data if he is deprived of the opportunity to personally check and correct his outpatient findings against the most reliable known method of obtaining the psychiatric history. This is by direct observation of the reenactment of past neurotic conflicts in stereotyped acting-out patterns in relationship to staff members in the residential unit. There are actually a number of other specific training advantages to inpatient experience with adolescents, as will be developed.

INPATIENT THERAPY

Each resident is currently assigned three (in the past four to five) inpatients and is held responsible for *all* aspects of each patient's care. The practice of vesting "administrative" and "psychotherapeutic" responsibilities in two separate therapists has, on the basis of our experience plus observation during my visits to many other inpatient units throughout the United States and Europe, proven for the most part to be unworkable with adolescent patients. This generalization seems a very sound one despite some apparent noteworthy exceptions, such as the Children's Hospital of the Menninger Clinic where a "two-doctor" approach is employed, but only to a degree and relatively late in the patient's hospitalization. The almost infinitely varied kinds of tasks which a resident will have in the treatment of an adolescent inpatient can, with unfortunate artificiality, be classified under two categories which are actually inseparably interrelated. These, for want of better terms, can be designated: (a) The Administration, and (b) The Psychotherapy.

Administration

Under "administrative" responsibilities (a term which is used reluctantly since in psychiatry it has become a widely misused and misunderstood cliche with unfortunate pejorative connotations) might be included many realistic services to the patient. Among these are numerous parentlike functions that any adolescent's therapist, as an adult of essential importance in the patient's life, is called upon to fulfill, such as to advise, to demand, to discipline, to teach, to prohibit, to give sometimes a spontaneous expression of personal feelings or opinion, or rarely a bit of angry fatherly hell-raising. All these may, of course, assume even greater importance in the case of the adolescent inpatient than for the outpatient. Also for the adolescent *inpatient* the therapist, as a hospital official, is in reality unavoidably responsible directly or indirectly, knowingly or not, for the patient's care and activities twenty-four hours a day, seven days a week—this is in addition to being psychotherapist and physician. One of his most important and challenging duties is making use of his psychologic knowledge of the patient to work with nurses, teachers, and other staff members to provide for the patient a stable and gratifying social environment and maximal opportunity for successful functioning in the required full-time school and other activities provided. He must also work constantly with other staff members in support of their efforts to resist the patient's need to recreate in this setting his old familiar pathologic ways of interacting with people. This requirement to work closely with many others provides for the resident major new challenges and opportunities for learning. Many important issues must be discussed with the entire staff group, so, to a degree, the therapist of a properly treated adolescent inpatient must work in a fishbowl.

As a result, if the resident is sensitive and curious, his own anxieties in this situation lead him to important lessons about himself, about psychotherapy, and about working with people which otherwise he might never learn. An illustrative example is seen in an experience of one of our brightest residents. Finding one of his supervisors working alone in his office, the resident interrupted to volunteer a report of something he had never brought to regular supervisory hours. He was feeling frustrated and puzzled by repeated questions concerning his patients from various nurses who appeared to remain dissatisfied with his answers to their questions, even though the doctor thought his replies had been thorough and clear. The supervisor suggested that he might cease responding to the content of the nurses' questions and inquire instead into what they might be feeling about him. This led to the resident finding time for an informal chat in the nursing office where he learned that many of the staff were very angry at him because "your patients always run away." They were projecting upon him their own feelings of frustration and inadequacy that they too felt helpless to prevent these patients from running away. Had the pain of the repeated disappearance of some of his patients together with the pressure of the nurses' questions, and of their hostility, not compelled this doctor to reexamine his own work for possible errors (which it had) he might have missed an added impetus to learning. Residents typically find it even more difficult to recognize such painful effects as hostility when coming from fellow workers than to face the anger of a patient in the familiar setting of the therapist's office. By the same token, such experiences in working with groups of people without benefit of the traditional psychiatrist's props, if successfully integrated, can be invaluable—particularly in light of current trends to call upon psychiatrists to work with community groups.

This, by the way, is the same resident who after three months' experience on the service had acquired the wisdom to observe for the benefit of fellow residents at a teaching conference: "No, disagreements among the staff do not undermine treatment, not if you can bring them out in the open and make them overt. It's the covert disagreements that lead to acting-out on the part of the staff, and that does undermine treatment."

Many decisions concerning treatment may be and are made by individual staff members, including the therapist. Some major decisions are made jointly by a group of staff people. We have found that a group of well-trained and reasonable people can ordinarily make mutually agreed-upon decisions, but only if all understand in advance whose judgment prevails should they disagree. In our system, this responsibility is the resident's. It is his job to coordinate, teach, supervise, and if need be, direct all the people working with his patient. He is the one who, with supervisory backing, is finally responsible for all decisions concerning the patient. He is also responsible for saying "yes" and "no" to his patient's requests. It follows that one of the most important of the many real services that the resident gives to the patient will be to provide help in controlling impulses. This involves sometimes imposing necessary restrictions, while in the meantime hopefully helping the patient ultimately to learn better to regulate his own impulses. This job of frustrating the patient by saying "no" to him is one which no one likes, and which runs contrary to certain exaggerated psychiatric traditions for permissiveness. It is one that the resident typically finds extremely difficult, and yet one which he cannot delegate entirely to others. In the inpatient setting with adolescents, perhaps better than in any other, the resident has the opportunity to learn what an essential role this kind of authoritative adult support plays in the development of all adolescents. He may also learn from actual experience a very basic and often forgotten principle of all psychotherapy—that no patient can profit by expressing his feelings verbally in psychotherapy unless first there is provided, in one way or another, reasonable assurance that these feelings will not be acted out dangerously either in the therapy or outside. The adolescent inpatient can teach the resident, as he has some of us, that in all psychotherapy, including even psychoanalysis, the therapist inevitably wields a simply enormous authoritative disciplinary influence on his patient. This he does either knowingly or unknowingly, by direct actions taken or by actions not taken. The resident has a rich opportunity to disprove the popular psychiatric myth that any psychotherapy can be authoritatively neutral. He can study the essential role which his authoritative influence as therapist is playing, and try to learn to use this knowledge flexibly in the interest of his patients' treatment.

Psychotherapy

This same resident "administrative disciplinary doctor" is also psychotherapist to his patient. It is true that each patient's maximal participation in school and other constructive activities receives, as it should, strong emphasis, as do details of his behavior and social relationships on the ward. As noted, some of the most important of the resident's therapeutic activities will be those devoted to promoting his patient's maximal success in these areas. It could even be said that the proper role of psychotherapy with the adolescent inpatient is, in a sense, one secondary to helping the patient select and succeed at various realistic achievement goals while in the hospital. It is also true that, in this setting at least, most of the patients are in group psychotherapy three hours per week, and some are in family therapy in addition.

Yet, for all these considerations, intensively supervised individual psychotherapy still plays an important role in the treatment program for the hospitalized adolescent, or should in most situations where staffing makes it available. Certainly in ours, or any setting where it is possible, it can and should play a key role in teaching and learning the dynamics of psychotherapy for which it provides an opportunity par excellence.

Psychotherapy of the adolescent inpatient is best planned in a very flexible manner according to the needs and capacities of the individual patient at the moment. Residents are taught to accept the challenge of setting aside many of the comforting psychiatric traditions for the regularly scheduled fifty-minute hour and so forth, in return for the learning opportunity of using a variety of approaches in psychotherapy. Newly admitted patients, for example, commonly need to be seen in relatively brief and very frequent interviews. While planning of therapy is highly individualized, in general the course of hospitalization for the typical patient is one of gradual de-emphasis of brief psychotherapeutic interventions to resolve crises, and toward more formal, scheduled, hour-long interviews of somewhat more conventional psychotherapy in the doctor's office.

It is true, as Farnsworth [1] once remarked, that nondirective psychotherapy of the adolescent makes about as much sense as nondirective surgery. At the same time, individual psychotherapy of these, like all patients, still necessarily involves a great deal of passive listening, observation of behavior, data-collecting, and suspension of judgment while awaiting the development of new facts wherever they may lead.

The dual responsibilities of administrator and therapist do, indeed, provide an enormous challenge for the resident. On the one hand, as an adult and a therapist, he must provide many very real functions including those of an administrator, and some parentlike ones such as being sometimes the frustrator and the disciplinarian. We expect this same doctor a moment later to behave as a more traditional psychotherapist. As noted, all residents find it difficult to say "no" to their patients, and most find it difficult to tolerate the ambiguity essential to exploratory psychotherapy. To ask that one inexperienced psychotherapist shift back and forth between one mode and the other, as the occasion may require, is sufficiently difficult that one could argue with much justification that this is imposing an unrealistic strain and source of confusion on him. However, the feelings of confusion resulting from these admittedly heavy demands for flexibility is necessary since the two approaches are inseparably interrelated. Not only are both crucial in the treatment of all adolescents, but some equivalent of both play an essential part in the psychotherapy of all patients. Thus, given a setting in which the resident can receive enough help to avoid being overwhelmed, he can learn from the start to integrate the use of "administrative" and "pyschotherapeutic" approaches in his therapy. He may, therefore, never have to unlearn, as many of us have, the false dichotomy of the traditional psychiatric myth that these two approaches can be neatly separated. Consequently, the resident's struggle to be this "Man of All Seasons" to his adolescent inpatient becomes a particularly dramatic and useful learning experience in preparation for future practice, even with patients who are not adolescents.

The doctor's dual role, along with the manner in which clear-cut hospital policy and abundant supervisory help can replace for the resident reliance on classical psychotherapeutic traditions, are illustrated in the following oversimplified clinical vignette:

> The patient was a fifteen-year-old boy originally hospitalized with a complaint of an odor emanating from his genital area (a belief shared only by his mother), and a diagnosis of paranoid schizophrenia. During treatment this delusional preoccupation had disappeared and had been absent for a short time when the boy began speaking to his doctor with a warning, "I have bad news for you." He then reported some new somatic delusional symptoms referable to the eyes—with associated fears of going blind. He presented this in support of his pressured request that he be permitted to save his eyes by remaining out of school. He correctly judged that this young doctor would be sufficiently frightened by this omnious-sounding psychotic symptom, that he would be unable to examine it matter-of-factly, determine its realistic clinical significance, or listen to the patient's feelings about it. This doctor, who had been

very frightened by the patient's psychosis and exquisitely relieved to see it improving, was, indeed, too shaken by this sudden appearance of the new symptom to talk with the patient about it. However, he felt sustained by the knowledge that it was the policy on the adolescent ward that all patients attend school regularly even though very ill, and that supervisors take a dim view of residents permitting patients to play hookey for any reason! He recovered his equilibrium in time to come up with the correct intuitive answer to the question about school, and assured the boy that he would remain in school. The patient, obviously more relieved than threatened by this demand, promptly returned to school. Later the resident was sufficiently relieved that neither blindness nor overwhelming psychosis had ensued, that he was able, with supervisory help, to re-evaluate his own anxiety. He could then successfully explore with the patient previously undiscussed fears of his psychosis, with the result that the new symptoms also disappeared.

TRANSFERENCE AND COUNTERTRANSFERENCE

The therapist's dual role accentuates the youngster's notorious need and exquisite skill in testing his therapist, as he does other adults, in terms of seeking out blind spots, idiosyncrasies, and neurotic traits. It is, of course, necessary for him to attempt to check out the doctor's ability to provide him with what he needs even in the face of his own inspired attempts to make that task as difficult as possible. The resident must struggle to make the various practical decisions concerning his patient's activities or therapy, while at the same time trying to listen to him, to understand him, and to help him to understand himself. The therapist finds himself on a hot seat as the patient "zeros" in on him to see if the doctor can succeed where parents (and the patient himself) have failed in the past. The therapist's skill, interest, and integrity in making these many varied, personal, and flexible decisions are the basis for therapy. The therapist must ponder his decisions, considering all the known facts about the patient. He does this either deliberately or with the fast, almost intuitive response, often either required by circumstances or inadvertently made, in the brand of "instant psychiatry" which these patients require. The exquisite transference-countertransference binds which consequently develop are so exaggerated and dramatic that they will leave the resident with little choice but to look hard at painful subjective reactions in himself.

An illustrative example is seen in the case of a pretty, seductive, hysterical, impulse-ridden, sixteen-year-old girl who had been admitted with a history of delinquent behavior and defiance of parental and other authorities. Observation in the hospital had demonstrated clearly that the stimulating social life of the ward led to excitement and overwhelming anxiety in her, culminating in running away from the hospital. As a result, she had been restricted to her room by her doctor. His ambivalence about making this decision had been somewhat clarified and his resolve bolstered by the strong opinion from other staff members. While so restricted she began to show improved functioning in other areas, such as in school and in psychotherapy. However, this unbelievably manipulative girl, sensing her doctor's doubts, subjected him to fantastic pressure to release the restrictions. She played upon every anxiety and guilt she could sense in him. She did this with well-orchestrated selections from her infinite repertoire of manipulative maneuvers. These varied all the way from simulated hallucinations accompanied by threats of regression into hopeless psychosis, to screaming accusations that he was a power-mad monster who relished exercising such controls over her. As a result of earlier experience with her, and with the help he received from fellow residents and other staff members as well as from supervisors, he managed to keep the situation somewhat in perspective and to hold the line for a time. However, he eventually wavered under fire and gradually began to reassure her that the restrictions would be lifted very soon. Immediately thereafter, the girl ran away again. This time she did not return until brought back several days later by her mother, from whom she had by then exacted a promise to remove her from the hospital against medical advice. There followed a midnight emergency family session with the doctor and social worker in which the girl pulled out all the stops to get the mother to follow through on this promise. The tortured mother finally conceded, "It's the wrong thing to do, but I can't stand this. I'll take you home." The girl then in desperation allowed herself a few words of honest verbal expression. She said, "You never disciplined me at home like the hospital is trying to do." This statement, although immediately followed by a renewed campaign of threats and tears, was sufficient to reactivate the mother's ambivalence—eventually leading to a decision to leave the girl in treatment. In this crisis the girl's behavior provided a dramatic lesson for the resident about what she was trying to do and why. Thereafter, he was much more able to be firm, and she began to conform to hospital restrictions. A short time later he observed to me, his supervisor, "I no longer feel guilty about frustrating her." I immediately questioned this, and thereafter he reported her new verbal attacks upon him for denying her a privilege. His response had consisted of a long series of explanations and re-assurances to the effect of "No, it is not so that I enjoy having power over you, it's just that I am doing what's best for you, etc., etc.!" He then needed but little help to see that his own behavior with the patient had belied his words, and that, in fact, he was still feeling guilty about what he knew he had to do, and very anxious over her criticisms of him. He finally remarked, "I never realized before now how important it is to be liked." Then after some discussion in supervision he came to the realization that such an exaggerated need to be liked was a general personality characteristic in him. It had tended to handicap all of his previous psychotherapeutic work, without his having been aware of it.

Such phenomena are quite analogous to what happens in all psychotherapy, of course. But adolescent patients, especially inpatients, have a way of demanding, with their behavior if words do not suffice, the doctor's attention to painful counter-transference realities in a way that makes them relatively undeniable. Among our residents, the adolescent service has been dubbed the "countertransference service." Residents' wives have traditionally been impressed, saying "Never has my husband been so involved with his patients until he came to the adolescent service." They have often commented, especially to my wife, about changes their husbands have undergone while working with hospitalized teenagers.

A kind of highly-mutual, progressive, educational process typically ensues between therapist and adolescent patient, especially the inpatient. This Hornick[2] has referred to as a process of "mutual maturation."

SUPERVISION

Assigning residents (sometimes even during the first year

of training) to such varied and complex responsibilities obviously calls for an enormously difficult and time consuming task for supervisors. There are obviously many possible approaches to the challenge of teaching the inpatient psychotherapy of the adolescent. The approach used on our service, along with some of the attendant problems, advantages, and findings can be summarized as follows:

1. All supervisors are senior psychiatrists, administrative officers on the service, who are full-time or nearly full-time. We have to date never employed part-time, outside consultants for supervision because of the conviction that the supervisor needs to have intimate knowledge of the situation in which the patient is being treated and in which the resident is working. As a result, while each resident accepts full responsibility for all aspects of his patient's treatment, he is not only taught by, but backed up by, the supervisor to whom he is responsible, and who shares with the resident full-time administrative responsibility for treatment. This arrangement, while obviously expensive in terms of staff time and therefore a luxury which cannot be afforded everywhere, is in our view ideal. It carries far more advantages than disadvantages. It means that some supervisor is always available for on-the-spot advice as sought by the residents pertaining to immediate decisions on crises with patients. It means that the supervisor has extensive knowledge of the patient, the resident, and the treatment in addition to that which the resident brings to the regularly scheduled supervisory hours. These hours, incidentally, number a minimun of three hours per week for each resident. For example, one resident protested his supervisor's observations on how his own subjective responses were interfering with treatment by complaining that it couldn't be true because he had received nothing but high ratings for his psychotherapy on other services where he had worked exclusively with outpatients. Then the supervisor suggested that "maybe the discrepancy stems from the fact that they knew nothing about your work except what you told them; I can still remember how sometimes as a resident I told the super-

visors what I thought they should know, if I could get away with it." To this, the resident could only reply with a sheepish "touché." After this, he settled down to consider seriously his supervisor's comments about his own countertransference difficulties, and how this new knowledge of himself might be utilized in improving the treatment of his patient.

This system presents disadvantages in that it can be threatening as well as educational for the resident to know that his work is subject to observation by his supervisor via many approaches. Consequently, it may be extremely difficult for the resident to feel willing and able to exercise independent judgments. It may, indeed, be correspondingly difficult for the supervisor to avoid being unduly paternalistic with the resident, and to wean him, as he must, to increasing responsibilities according to his realistic capacities and level of experience.

2. On this service, most patients are treated by residents. However, it is a regular practice for each supervisor to carry an inpatient himself, for whom he is fully responsible in the same manner as the resident. Thus, since details of all aspects of each patient's treatment, including for the most part what happens in psychotherapy, are discussed regularly with all members of the staff, then each resident has the opportunity to learn by observing how his supervisor handles clinical problems comparable to those with which he is struggling. He can hear or see how the supervisor handles situations with other staff members as well as directly with patients. He will have an opportunity to see how senior psychiatrists also are regularly seduced by adolescent patients into subjectively determined lapses in clinical judgment. He may observe how his teachers attempt to extricate themselves and their patients from these painful dilemmas. He will have a chance to observe how regularly and deliberately we make use in teaching of these recurrent living proofs of our own human fallibility. This is done, for example, in helping other staff members to accept and learn from similar "mistakes" in themselves. The resident can see how we try to exploit in psychotherapy these errors on

our part, to which the patient out of his own neurotic needs has almost invariably contributed. We can try to help the patient to understand his own past distorted relationships with people, as these are now projected upon the therapist in transference, and made manifest in the therapist's "counter-transference" errors.

The practice of senior staff treatment of inpatients is in our department almost unique to the adolescent service. From what I have been able to gather, it is quite exceptional in teaching hospitals generally. It is remarkable, and I think regrettable, that most of the inpatient psychiatry done by residents in teaching hospitals is taught by psychiatrists who have not personally taken responsibility for an inpatient for many years. We do it partly to provide an example for the resident. But we also feel that the intense emotional experiences through which the therapist of an adolescent inpatient goes are sometimes so painful and therefore readily repressible (and rerepressible) that a supervisor who is not regularly meeting these challenges in his own practice would be seriously hand-icapped in his attempts to understand what the resident is going through.

3. The fact that each resident and supervisor has, at once, administrative and psychotherapeutic responsibilities for patients is determined by our viewpoint that this provides maximum advantages both in terms of treatment and resident training, at least in most cases. This arrangement, incidentally, tends to promote an intense reliving of adolescent conflicts on the part of the patient and, to a degree, on the part of the resident, and sometimes even on the part of the supervisor. As a result, the patient gets, hopefully, a flexible variety of adult and psychotherapeutic responses as he may require them. The resident, and the supervisor too, get a particularly concentrated course on how conflicts are manifested, managed, and resolved in psychotherapy. Frequently rather intense transference-countertransference situations develop between resident and supervisor, oftentimes paralleling those between resident and patient. These may require interpretative exam-

ination together in order that the resident and preceptor may once again attend more efficiently to the clinical problems between patient and resident. These exchanges with residents, some of which are quite heated initially, I have found to be highly educational. From them I have learned a great deal from residents about residents, about patients, and often about myself. In other words, I would elaborate on Hornick's concept to add that a "mutual maturation" process also goes on between resident and preceptor.

An illustration is seen in the events stemming from an incident involving a brief, abortive bout of fisticuffs between two boys on our adolescent ward—this being behavior which is considered quite unacceptable in that setting. The therapist of the more passive of these two boys was an unusually gifted, perceptive and well-trained senior resident in psychiatry, although new on the adolescent service. After inquiring into the incident in an interview with his patient, he arrived at the conclusion that the boy was the innocent victim of an unprovoked attack. There then followed an intense period in which this doctor quarreled violently with the resident who was treating the other boy, the theme of this quarrel being, "How could you let your patient attack my patient like this? And now, what are you going to do to him?" More significantly still, the first resident quarreled with his supervisors, particularly with me, the chief of service. He blamed me for not resolving this quarrel to his satisfaction, and especially for making such unjust ward rules that forbade patients from even defending themselves when attacked. Eventually, after some long, mutually painful supervisory sessions he recognized his identification with his patient's wish to fight surreptitiously in opposition to the established order. After he had discussed some of his own resentment toward me and toward the ward program he was able to reinterview his patient, this time permitting the boy to reveal additional facts. These facts made it immediately apparent to both that this patient had deliberately provoked the other, more aggressive boy into hitting him first. The resident's eventual sheepish summary of his own reaction was, "So my patient picks a fight on the ward, and I congratulate him for it, all in the good cause of getting even with my chief!" Not long after that, in another incident, this same very articulate resident returned the favor by giving me a lesson. Feeling frustrated and puzzled by his failure to recognize something obvious, I persisted long and loud in a fruitless attempt to show him where he was wrong—finally giving up, more from exhaustion than out of any wisdom on my part. Later, he observed, "You would have saved yourself a lot of trouble by just keeping quiet and letting me talk. I was so far off base I would have hanged myself in nothing flat and would have done your job for you."

SUMMARY AND CONCLUSIONS

The degree of emphasis given on this service to inpatient treatment as compared to outpatient work represents partly a deliberate judgment with regard to proper priorities. It is also partly an inadvertent expression of my own special interest. (Incidentally, we are at present in the process of expanding treatment and training in the outpatient area, while hopefully not letting work with inpatients suffer.)

Certainly, experience with the adolescent inpatients should be a part of the training of all psychiatrists who anticipate working with adolescents, even though their subsequent practice be exclusively with outpatients. It is quite essential for those who specialize in the field of adolescent psychiatry. Furthermore, work with adolescent inpatients has a very special contribution to make to the general training of psychiatrists, even though they may not subsequently see teenage patients at all. As noted, working with the adolescent inpatient provides a particularly concentrated and dramatic demonstration of some of the dynamics of psychotherapy. It provides the best of opportunities to observe one's countertransference reactions. The young psychiatrist can thus learn more of his own particular style of life, his idiosyncrasies, his resources, and neurotic blindspots—all in the interest of becoming a more sophisticated therapist in the future. It presents an enforced opportunity to observe and work with the reality aspects of one's relationship to the patient. This must be done while at the same time dealing in an exploratory, and as indicated, an interpretative way with transference phenomena through which the patient's emotional conflicts are also manifested, and hopefully resolved in therapy. As noted, the two closely interrelated aspects of treatment—the "administrative" and the "psychotherapeutic" are universal to all therapy. This is not generally recognized, and can be better appreciated after experience with hospitalized adolescents. These patients also offer an especially clear demonstration of another important attribute of all psychotherapy—the gradual progressive weaning of the patient ultimately to do for himself what initially needs be done for him by the therapist. In the course of such weaning of his patient, the resident has a ringside seat for direct observation of some important phases of adolescent psychological development.

Adolescent patients are among the world's best teachers of psychiatry, and the average adolescent inpatient potentially merits an honorary professorship in practical psychotherapy.

REFERENCES *

1. Farnsworth, Dana L.: Comment at Timberlawn Psychiatric Center, Dallas, Texas, 1969, quoted by Joe W. King, M.D.
2. Hornick, Edward: Panel on "Transference and Countertransference," Annual meeting, American Psychiatric Association, Atlantic City, May, 1967.
3. Miller, A. A., and Sabshin, M.: Psychotherapy in psychiatric hospitals. *Arch Gen Psychiat, 9*:53–65, 1963.
4. Miller, A. A., and Burstein, A. G.: Professional development in psychiatric residents. *Arch Gen Psychiat, 20*:385–394, 1969.
5. Ekstein, R., and Wallerstein, R. S.: *The Teaching and Learning of Psychotherapy*. N.Y., Basic Books, 1958.
6. Hendrickson, W. J.; Holmes, D. J., and Waggoner, R. W.: Psychotherapy with hospitalized adolescents. *Amer J Psychiat, 116*:527–532, 1959.
7. Holmes, D. J.: *Psychotherapy of the Adolescent*. Boston, Little Brown, 1964.
8. Escoll, P. J., and Wood, H.P.: Perception in residency training: methods and problems. *Amer J Psychiat, 124*:2, 1967.
9. Pederson, W. M.: Personal communication, 1969.

---

* References include works not directly cited within the text.

Chapter Three

Training of Psychiatric Residents
in a Student Mental Health Clinic

ROBERT L. ARNSTEIN
JOHN P. PLUNKETT

RAINING OF PSYCHIATRISTS in the specialty of college psychiatry is probably an appropriate topic for a conference
on training in adolescent psychiatry. We say probably because
college and university students are clearly on the outgoing
end of the period of adolescence, and there are some perhaps
who would feel that the decision to include them at all in the
adolescent period is questionable. When describing our patient
population, we usually state that they are "in the late adolescent and young adult categories." This is unwieldy but somewhat more precise than calling them all adolescents or all
adults, because we offer services to the entire university student
body, which includes both undergraduates and graduates in
an age range of approximately seventeen to twenty-six. It
has occasionally been suggested that a special developmental
period designation should be applied to this stage of life, but
so far at least no such designation has caught on popularly,
and it is questionable whether it truly deserves a separate
label as a developmental period even though the state of being
a student may add special conditions.

Let us look briefly at the history of college psychiatry because it is only against this background that one can accurately
understand the development and current state of training in
this particular subspeciality. Although Dr. Stewart Paton
at Princeton in 1910 is usually cited as the first college psychiatrist, it was not really until the 1920's that anything more

than sporadic attempts to establish psychiatric services on college campuses occurred. In the 1920's, however, services were instituted at several colleges, and some, at least, were established firmly enough so that continuity developed, with psychiatrists devoting their time and thinking on a full-time basis to the problems of student psychiatry. Some, such as the Menningers and Austen Riggs, were among the most illustrious psychiatrists in the nation; others limited their work to the field of college psychiatry but within this sphere had tremendous influence. The latter included Theophile Raphael at Michigan, and closer to home, Clements Fry, who came to Yale in 1926 and remained until his death in 1955. During this time Dr. Fry laid the foundation for all aspects of our current service. During the 1920's and early 1930's there was considerable theoretical concern about the major purpose of work with students. The name "Mental Hygiene" which is still attached to our clinic is probably a remainder of a general philosophy which propounded the idea that students might benefit from counseling and therapy whether or not they showed clearcut psychopathology, the benefit visualized in terms of personality development and preparation for future life growth. In some quarters there was considerable criticism of conventional psychiatry which, using a medical model, presumably characterized people as ill before treatment was considered appropriate. Dr. Fry, up until the time of his death, even though a trained psychiatrist, preferred that the individuals coming to the service be designated as "students" rather than patients.

Although the 1920's saw college psychiatry firmly established, the depression and consequent shortages of funds reduced many services to minimal operations, and there resulted relatively little development or expansion during the 1930's. Those services that survived attempted to deal with the more major illnesses which developed on campus, and inevitably gave less attention to the less urgent conditions. World War II stripped almost all campuses of psychiatric help, but also focussed on the importance of psychiatric treatment and the efficacy of brief treatment. In the post-World War II period the great upsurge of interest in psychiatry as a speciality had a considerable impact on student services, and gradually many of the services that existed or were started became relatively conventional psychiatric clinics with emphasis on psychotherapy in one or another of its forms, and a consequent tendency to view those who came as patients. At many colleges "counseling services" had developed concurrently and sometimes the Health Department service was seen as dealing with more serious problems inasmuch as a psychiatrist was involved.

Two factors particularly influenced the Yale development. First, no counseling service existed so that those students who needed professional help came to the Health Department. Secondly, a psychoanalytic orientation became paramount in the late 1940's. At that time Drs. Margaret Brenman and Robert Knight came to the service as consultants, and they were followed by Dr. Alfred Gross, who acted as chairman of the clinical conference for several years before his death. These names are mentioned simply to indicate that the psychoanalytic influence was historically important in the clinic's development, and understandably influenced the kind of therapy used and taught. This influence coincided with the appointment of Dr. Fredrick Redlich as Chairman of the Yale Department of Psychiatry, and a general shift to a psychoanalytic orientation in the Medical School.

The expansion of the Yale program into training occurred in the late 1940's. Dr. Fry for some time had felt that an expansion of the service to include training and research activities was desirable, and he did what he could to institute these. An endowment from the Old Dominion Foundation in the early 1950's made possible the undertaking of a formal training program and in 1957 application for a USPHS training grant was made to continue the program on an expanded scale. The training program has always been under the direction and development of our service, but is accredited through the Yale Department of Psychiatry. In the initial ten years of the program the training consisted mainly of experience in seeing student patients on a once-a-week basis, with emphasis on psychoanalytically-oriented psychotherapy, backed up by individual supervision and attendance at a weekly staff conference which alternated between clinical presentations and topic presentations of general interest to members of the staff.

The formal application to NIMH described the goals of the program: "The program is designed to provide advanced training for third- and fourth-year psychiatric trainees: (1) in the specialized area of college psychiatry; (2) in the technique of out-patient psychotherapy, both individual and group; (3) in aspects of providing a mental health service for a specific community; and (4) in the theory of late adolescent development." Since then no major changes have been made in the training program, but it has gradually evolved into a far more complex and organized program as we have added courses and refined various aspects. The full-time program was initially conceived as, and has remained, a program for third- and fourth-year fellows (residents). We feel that a minimum of two years of prior training is essential because of the degree of responsibility required of any therapist in our service.

Currently the program is divided into three or four segments. The core is the clinical work, which includes initial evaluation, individual psychotherapy, group psychotherapy, supervision and emergency coverage. This occupies a little more than 50 percent of the fellow's time. The didactic program, which includes mainly seminars plus one or two large staff conferences, occupies approximately a quarter of the fellow's time, and the remaining quarter is divided between research and miscellaneous activities. Most of our third-year fellows have a five-hour child psychiatry commitment, which is part of the Department of Psychiatry progression in child psychiatry training, under the auspices of the Child Study Center. Fourth-year residents who have completed their child psychiatry commitment use the five hours for consultation, research, or other special elective work.

Although one might like to think that training in psychiatry at any college would be similar to training at any other, clearly campuses vary and inevitably affect the training experience. The general atmosphere of Yale as a university is well known. It has a student population of approximately nine thousand and it is highly selective as far as admission is concerned. The student body is equally divided between an undergraduate college, which, until this year, has been all-male, and a graduate population distributed between several graduate and professional schools. Historically, the undergraduate college has been the dominant school, and it is almost totally residential divided into twelve "residential" colleges. These house almost all upper classmen and have affiliated freshmen, who live in a separate quadrangle. In recent years the graduate and professional schools have tended to increase in size, influence, and general involvement in campus matters. The graduate students live partially in dormitories, and partially off-campus.

The Division of Student Mental Hygiene is a unit of the Department of University Health, which is an autonomous administrative unit under the Provost's Office. The Mental Hygiene Division staff consists of three essentially full-time psychiatrists, eight part-time psychiatrists, three clinical psychologists, three psychiatric social workers, a part-time sociologist, who acts as research coordinator, and a part-time speech therapist. The service offers diagnosis and evaluation, non-intensive individual psychotherapy, group psychotherapy, conjoint therapy and speech therapy on an outpatient basis. An infirmary can be used for students in mildly disturbed states, but if psychiatric hospitalization is necessary this must be effected at the Yale-New Haven Medical Center. All students are eligible, as are student spouses, for all aspects of the service. Faculty and employees are eligible for consultation and referral only. Over a ten-year period the number of students who have used the service annually increased from 7 percent of the total student body to approximately 11 percent in the last academic year. Over the same period the percentage of students coming self-referred has increased from 37 percent to 70 percent.

The training program begins in the summer with a three-week orientation period which includes a series of seminars about the college and the history of college mental health. It includes a reading seminar and seminars on initial evaluation and on psychological testing. In addition there are sessions in which the Policy and Procedure Manual of the clinic is reviewed and discussed. In discussion of the latter much of the operating philosophy of the service is covered.

The clinical experience is composed of three parts—evaluation, therapy, and the handling of emergencies. All trainees have four hours each week set aside for intake interviews. The student who comes in to the clinic is seen initially for an intake interview usually within forty-eight hours. At that time the problem is assessed and a decision and recommendation made. If therapy is indicated the student is then assigned for therapy with either the initial interviewer or with someone else on the clinic staff. Obviously, the initial evaluation must take into account several factors. The student's situation must be evaluated in terms of the nature and urgency of his problem, his psychopathology, those factors which motivate and influence his coming to the clinic, his ability to cope with his academic responsibilities, and the treatment of choice. There are, of course, other considerations of a practical nature that have to be assessed. Because at certain times there is a wait for therapy assignment, the student's ability to wait has to be ascertained. This latter evaluation needs to be made not only in terms of the degree of psychiatric urgency, but also in terms of the relative administrative urgency. In many instances, if a student is going to retain his student status help must come rapidly.

Once therapy has been decided on there is a choice of individual or group therapy. Although the majority of students are seen individually, the clinic has had a group therapy program for over fifteen years under the direction of Dr. Walter Igersheimer and all fellows are encouraged to participate. Individual therapy is limited to one semester of weekly sessions for "elective" therapy. The term "elective" is elusive and is somewhat loosely defined, but without such a limit we found that we would be unable to see anyone in therapy after about January first. Some students are seen for much longer and occasionally some are seen more than once a week, but this is unusual. When indicated, however, a student may be seen several times a week to help him through a crisis period.

The emergency coverage is similar to other emergency on call duty except that the psychiatrist must be prepared to go anywhere on the campus if necessary. Usually patients in off-hours are seen at the Infirmary, but occasionally emergency interviews are conducted in more unusual surroundings. We feel that the handling of emergencies is an important part of the service on any campus and this experience is a significant part of training. In the handling of any emergency the community aspect of college psychiatry becomes particularly evident. In addition to dealing with the upset student, it may be necessary to deal with family, roommates, deans, etc., and any failure to communicate appropriately with all involved individuals is usually immediately apparent.

Although much of the psychotherapy is not so different from any goal-limited psychoanalytically oriented psychotherapy, there are certain theoretical premises which underlie the therapy, particularly as it relates to undergraduates. One of these premises is that life experience is an important therapeutic force and that frequently a small amount of therapy will allow the individual to continue with his natural development. Furthermore, the college experience is an important aspect of this developmental phase. This suggests that the goals of therapy may be rather modest and that "cures," be they transference, flight into health, or whatever, may be accepted as real—real in the sense that one is not assuming that a major psychodynamic shift has occurred but rather that even a minor shift may allow the developmental thrust to continue. Thus, the student may reappear at the clinic in a year or so for additional therapy. We have tended to call this "discontinuous therapy" and feel that it is an appropriate treatment approach. In other words, a series of brief contacts over more than one year may be more effective than a series of interviews of intermediate length.

A second premise has to do with issues concerned with emancipation from the family. While certain problems presented by the younger college student may be quite similar to those seen in the older adolescent in the family setting, the fact that the student is living away from home in the college environment may make a significant difference in the treatment situation. The student, in fact, *is* more independent and *does* have fewer restrictions imposed upon him. This is a desirable state of affairs and one of its applications is that he should have the opportunity of seeking treatment on his own without the knowledge of or financial dependence upon his family. This has led us to adhere to a policy of confidentiality which we feel is essential for establishing a favorable environment for dealing with many of the emancipation issues as well as other issues that arise in treatment. At a time when the student is struggling for greater independence but is still bound to the family by many of his emotional as well as realistic needs, he can experience this opportunity to seek help on his own as an act of real independence.

A third premise is that, in most instances, the state of being in college is a useful and desirable one for the student. Therefore, considerable effort will be made to provide supportive therapy simply to prolong that state, if possible. This does not mean, however, that we feel that all students should invariably remain in college at all costs, and a number of recommendations are made to students that they drop out of college for shorter or longer periods. It does mean that a considerable amount of attention gets focussed at times on very short range goals of resolving emotional conflicts interfering with academic progress because it is our belief that completion of an academic unit, whether it be the B.A. degree or a professional degree, does represent a considerable asset for the individual, and, therefore, it is desirable both because it enhances his feeling of self-worth and because, particularly, it may move him along toward an independent life position. On the other hand, there are times when the student obviously is not able to function and then time off is clearly indicated and may actually allow the individual to prepare sucessfully for completing college or to decide that it is not for him.

The fellow in training sees a wide range of clinical problems which are characteristic of the seventeen to twenty-six year age group. The majority probably are related to what we frequently call "self-concerns,"—feelings of inadequacy, stemming largely from difficulty in dealing with social and sexual relations. On the other hand, particularly in the older age range, one meets with a series of fairly well crystallized neurotic problems. In addition, there are a number of students in temporary psychotic states or borderline states. Because the university curriculum in certain cases is sufficiently flexible so that one can get along academically for a time at a fairly low level of functioning, these students may survive in the college environment for a considerable period. Furthermore, there are a number of students who are probably chronically psychotic or borderline in many areas of their functioning, but who are able to manage academically and these, of course, may be carried in treatment for a long period. Those of us who have worked steadily in the clinic never cease to be surprised by the wide variety of problems. In addition to well defined neuroses as well as psychoses and borderline states, we see drug reactions of all sorts; sexual problems ranging from concerns over heterosexual adequacy and homosexuality to transvestism, voyeurism, and fetishism; speech difficulties; urination difficulties, including a rare case of continued enuresis; and occasional conversion reactions.

Beyond these general kinds of problems, there are one or two that are more or less specific to the campus setting. Particularly in the undergraduate group, college is a time of decision about career. On a campus like Yale, where one has to have a fairly high demonstrable potential in order to get in, choice of career is a rather open one, and a good many students feel very uncertain about the choice. The uncertainty goes beyond a simple decision between law, medicine, business, engineering, or teaching, but includes the whole problem of life direction. Students who have more or less automatically gone through the process of college admission on the basis that college itself is a goal, may find themselves in considerable confusion about their ultimate direction. We are not sure this is necessarily a psychiatric problem, but it frequently gets mixed up with self-concerns and with issues connected with self-definition and emancipation and, therefore, often presents as a problem in therapy. A second problem is that of the graduate student who has finished his routine course work or lab work but finds it difficult to complete his thesis. Again, the rather special setting of Yale is involved. Although there are some masters candidates, and recently a degree of M.Ph. was instituted for those who had completed all requirements towards a Ph.D. except a dissertation, the general climate puts considerable pressure on a student to complete the full Ph.D. program. Similarly, in the Medical School and the Law School there are thesis and thesis-like requirements, and not infrequently a student has very real difficulty in completing this work. A third problem relating to graduate students involves difficulties stemming from the prolongation of student status. This may result in the continuing presence of issues having to do with the attainment of full independence which traditionally should have been resolved by or soon after the end of adolescence. This may give rise to many problems including those most frequently encountered when the student is married and conflicts arise between academic demands and family responsibilities.

To return to the training program per se, in order to gain as much training benefit as possible from the clinical experience each fellow has two hours of supervision a week for individual therapy and one hour of supervision for group therapy. In addition, there is a weekly continuous case conference of one and one-half hours conducted by Roy Schafer with two cases being presented, one every other week. Inasmuch as two new cases are presented during the second semester, this means that four of the fellows will have the opportunity to participate as presenter in the conference. All supervision is performed by senior staff members and we have been rather strict, if not rigid, about qualifying staff members for supervisory roles. The supervision usually is done by the presentation of therapy process notes for an individual patient, although there are some variations in how individual supervisors and fellows work. The supervision in our program is probably not different from supervision elsewhere so perhaps no more needs to be said about it.

There is a weekly Clinical Problems Conference conducted by the Director of Clinical Service and Training, attended by the fellows, members of the social work and clinical psychology staff as well as some of the staff psychiatrists. This gives the fellows, as well as the staff members, an opportunity to bring up current clinical problems and issues for discussion and management recommendations. During the course of the year each fellow presents two cases at the biweekly Clinical Staff Conference. Other staff members, including senior staff members who see patients, also present at the conference. This gives the fellow the rather unique opportunity not only of presenting, but also of being able to ask questions about and discuss the psychotherapeutic work of more experienced therapists.

As has already been mentioned, approximately ten hours are devoted to seminars of one sort or another, including the continuous case seminar and the clinical problems seminar. There is a seminar on ego psychology given by Ernest Prelinger stressing late adolescent development which runs throughout most of the year. It is constructed to relate ego development to psychotherapeutic issues. There is a weekly group therapy conference which discusses the theory and practice of group therapy. A general staff conference alternates with the clinical presentation and covers subjects of general interest. These might include visiting speakers, who may work on other college campuses, as well as experts in some field of particular relevance, such as drug abuse. Sometimes fellows who have graduated from our program, or staff members who have moved elsewhere, will return to discuss their new experiences. In addition, other university officials are invited to the conference to describe their areas of operation and to discuss problems of mutual interest. (On three occasions we have been fortunate to have Dr. Anna Freud present at four conferences.) Each fellow is responsible for one didactic presentation at this conference during the year. The didactic presentation is expected to be a review of the literature on some topic with the aim of (a) making the fellow responsible for looking up and organizing a specific body of material; and (b) educating our staff in recent developments in the literature on one or another subject of interest. These have been exceedingly well done over the years, and in several instances a fellow has used his didactic presentation as the basis of an article which was later published. Subjects covered have included mourning, examination anxiety, adverse reactions to marijuana, and the use of antidepressant drugs, to name a few.

We have also encouraged each fellow to engage in research. This is not a basic requirement, but we do make it clear that we would like at least an attempt at research, and some have done this very successfully. Our training year is, unfortunately, not ideally set up for this. The fellows have considerable time during the summer months, but at that time usually do not have clearly in mind what they might like to do. By midyear, when research ideas are numerous, the work pressure has increased so much that it is often difficult for a fellow to start and finish a project. Many interesting small projects, however, have been completed and several others have been worked on although they have not reached actual fruition. Several results of research projects have been published, including papers on "Student Use of Hallucinogens," "Academic Decline," "Readmission after Psychiatric Leave," and "Use of Hallucinogenic Drugs on Campus." There is a research conference in which all members of the staff present material concerned with research in progress. This gives the fellows opportunity not only to discuss their own projects but also to criticize work of staff members.

Although it is not always possible or desirable to make a

sharp distinction between clinical and administrative function in considering particular problems, one special aspect of college psychiatry, that of the consultative or community function, is dealt with primarily in the Administrative Seminar. This weekly conference is conducted by the Chief Psychiatrist, who presents problems with a consultative or administrative aspect. These are usually problems which he is currently facing and has not yet resolved. There is no attempt to cover in an organized fashion a comprehensive range of problems in a given year, although experience has shown that most of the problems one would want to talk about do tend to crop up naturally over the course of the year. There seems to have been considerable benefit in using the direct "unsolved problem" method, because it means that problems can be discussed as they are actually developing, with the fellows expressing their opinions and often influencing the action that is taken. This method also allows the fellows to see how a staff member thinks about some of the problems that arise and to compare their own thoughts with his. As one can imagine, the problems vary widely, but have included issues of confidentiality, policies about campus rules, plans for developing a new university health service, issues of research cooperation with nonuniversity resources, and the planning of talks to various university or other groups. It may include particularly difficult clinical emergencies, stressing not so much the clinical management of the emergency as issues of communication with university personnel, family, and hospital. This has been a very successful seminar and at the moment the agenda is so crowded that we will not have a chance to discuss half the subjects that should be covered.

In discussing the training program with our current group of fellows, we asked their views about shortcomings in the program. Two points were made. The first involved the conflict of interest arising between service needs and training considerations. By this they meant that ideally more opportunity should be made available for longer term, intensive treatment of patients selected primarily on the basis of what their treatment would offer to the training experience of the fellows. This is a valid criticism and we would prefer to be in a position to meet this ideal requirement. Inevitably, however, it is necessary to take care of the needs of the student population in the fairest and most consistent means possible and this does for the most part determine policy. What may be lost in learning outpatient psychotherapy, however, may be somewhat offset by the gain in learning college psychiatry, because we feel that for a resident spending one year in a training program the best way to learn about college students and their problems as well as about the college environment itself is for him to be able to see as broad a cross-section of the clinic caseload as he possibly can. Our program is designed to do just that.

Secondly, there was some feeling that the program did not offer sufficient possibilities for direct involvement in broad campus social issues which could be construed to have mental health implications. This is also a fair criticism but one which stems from two considerations, one practical and one theoretical. The practical consideration results from the fact that Yale is a relatively small institution in terms of the way it functions. Thus, when requests are made for psychiatric participation on committees or in discussion groups, it is usually for a specific individual and it is difficult to substitute a fellow in order to give him the training experience. The theoretical consideration has to do with our philosophy concerning involvement in controversial issues. Although we do not think that silence or neutrality is always desirable, we feel that active public advocacy of a particular point of view may influence indirectly the willingness of some students to utilize our service, and we think this is of primary importance. Thus, encouragement of random participation in campus activities which may be construed as representing clinic policy may have unpredictable ramifications of a more general and potentially undesirable nature.

We hope, of course, that we have achieved our aim of offering a well-balanced program which not only provides a grounding in college psychiatry but also inculcates a sound basic skill in conducting outpatient psychotherapy primarily of a short-term variety. The program has evolved gradually and we hope to keep improving it. Soon a new university health building will open and will include a new Infirmary facility which should allow broader experimentation with brief inpatient stays for somewhat more disturbed patients. We will continue to add other subjects or programs as they seem to fill a need. Our pace of change has been slow and some might feel that our program is too conservative, but we feel that the evolutionary process has created an atmosphere of stability, which is conducive to learning. Inasmuch as our training program is a vital and integral part of our total service, we think that this stability is important, not only for training but also for the service we provide to the student body.

Chapter Four

A Proposal for a Training Program in Adolescent Psychiatry in a Large City Hospital

ROBERT E. GOULD

THE FOLLOWING is a description of the training program in adolescent psychiatry at Bellevue Hospital. This was prepared two years ago for prospective residents. I offer it as an example of an adequate, perhaps even good and comprehensive program. And then I would like to suggest what I think an adolescent training program should be like today.

TRAINING IN ADOLESCENT PSYCHIATRY—PROGRAM OFFERED IN 1967

The first adolescent unit in a psychiatric hospital in this country was opened in Bellevue Psychiatric Hospital on April 1, 1937. This was a boys' ward which housed from forty to sixty patients between the ages of twelve and sixteen, most of whom were admitted through New York City courts. A separate service for adolescent girls was established thirteen years later, in 1950. Each ward was staffed by two full-time psychiatrists, a staff psychologist, sometimes an intern psychologist and generally three or four residents.

During the past ten years, there has been a rapid increase of professional interest in adolescent psychiatry, partly as a result of population changes which indicate an enormous growth in the number of adolescents, and the increasing need to develop special skills for working with youngsters in this age group. It has become obvious that the techniques necessary to deal with adolescents are different from the skills needed to work with either children or adults, and the training program is designed to develop these special techniques. Even for those psychiatrists who, after residency training, do not choose to work with adolescents, a more complete knowledge of the adolescent stage and of its vast range of pathology and problems will be of invaluable help in working with adults.

In the early history of the adolescent service, the heaviest emphasis was on diagnosis, evaluation and disposition of the patient. Through the years, the service has moved in the direction of offering more comprehensive care. During the average inpatient stay, four to six weeks, the adolescent is exposed to a variety of therapeutically oriented programs so that the milieu as a whole functions as a therapeutic modality. The service includes recreation and occupational therapy programs and a social work and psychology staff. The latter, in addition to their testing and interviewing roles, function in group therapy settings with both patient and parent groups.

To provide more continuity of treatment, as well as to augment training in long-term therapy on an inpatient basis, about one-fourth of the boys and girls on the wards are kept in the hospital for long-term treatment (three months to two years). The goal of this program is to return the patient to his community. In cases where this is not possible, the aim is to place the patient in a residential treatment center, where he would be likely to receive more therapy than in a state hospital.

Adolescent Psychiatry Training for General Psychiatric Residents is offered during the second year of the basic program when the resident is assigned to treat both adolescent inpatients on the wards and adolescent outpatients receiving long-term psychotherapy in the mental hygiene clinic, under the supervision of full-time staff psychiatrists. During his third year of training the resident may continue therapy with the adolescent patients he has been treating. The resident is responsible for the complete psychiatric evaluation and treatment of his patients, and for presenting his patients at case conferences. He receives supervision from the staff on the wards and in the clinic. In addition, he receives one hour per week of individual supervision of the adolescents he carries in long-term treatment.

The residents spend between four and six months on the adolescent service, caring for selected male and female patients from the two twenty-five-bed wards in short-term therapy. Additional patients on the wards are selected for long-term treatment. These youngsters are among those who would ordinarily be placed in state hospitals or training schools, but who, it is felt, have the potential for improving and making a good adjustment. A flexible school program has been established to answer the special needs of individual patients, and a teacher has been assigned exclusively to this group.

Residents also have the opportunity to do group therapy on a short-term basis. All trainees are encouraged to participate in this program so as to have some experience with this mode of treatment and to learn about group dynamics.

All residents are required to attend New Admission and Disposition Conferences. At the former, the new admissions are briefly discussed by the staff, residents and social workers to clarify what data are needed from other hospitals, agencies, schools and families. From the admission data decisions are made for a tentative general approach to the work-up of the patient and a delineation of tasks. Cases that are a week or two old are also briefly reviewed to consider modifications or additions to the initial plan. These conferences facilitate communication between social workers, residents and staff, and encourage a more intensive and complete work-up of each patient. They also provide the residents an opportunity to see how each phase of the work-up and treatment is approached, since they sit in on all cases, not just their own.

Once a week there is a disposition conference which the staff, residents, social worker, psychologist, nurses, school teacher, recreation worker and nurses' aides are expected to attend. The resident presents his case in depth and the others contribute their particular knowledge of the patient. This gives a good picture of the total functioning of the patient in all aspects of his daily life. Although the final decision about disposition is made by the senior full-time staff psychiatrist, after discussion of the case by the staff, the resident is encouraged to go through all the steps and make his own decision first. Residents attend the disposition conferences for all cases on the service.

Residents also attend a weekly case conference where the presentation will be centered on a particular problem, such as diagnosis, treatment, or dynamics. Residents are expected to participate in the discussions which are led by the chief of whichever service is presenting a case.

In addition, the chief of the adolescent service conducts a lecture and reading course for residents training in this unit. Reading is assigned each week, and because of the small group participating (5 to 8 people) this is a good opportunity for active participation.

Every six to eight weeks, residents are expected to visit various institutions to which Bellevue adolescent patients may be sent. These field trips acquaint the resident (and staff) with the various facilities available so that each patient may be placed in the most suitable environment. Furthermore, it enables the resident to speak in a more informed manner to parents concerning placement of their children.

RESEARCH ACTIVITIES

The adolescent unit sponsors a variety of research activities in which residents are encouraged to participate both during their second-year rotation and their third-year elective time. Among the projects now underway and planned are the following:

1. *An evaluation of the techniques and results of long-term therapy with inpatients.* Various projects have been undertaken utilizing different combinations of cotherapists working with adolescent groups.

2. *Court study.* A study of all court cases is in progress in order to clarify and evaluate the roles of the psychiatrist, probation officer and judge in relation to court referrals and

disposition of adolescents remanded to our service. Follow-up studies of youngsters discharged from Bellevue will be done to aid in evaluating the handling of each patient.

Ongoing research activities include:

3. *Clairol study.* The original study of high-school girls from disadvantaged urban backgrounds has revealed interesting data about their mental health and personality structure. We hope to compare the group already studied with a group of inpatients from similar backgrounds to learn more about the causative factors in mental illness.

4. *Study of violence.* This study is designed to elucidate some of the etiological factors in the production of violence in male adolescents.

5. *Research on hippies.* Through the use of question-naires and clinical evaluations, we will attempt to determine if there are psychodynamic factors in this group which set them apart from other adolescents.

6. *Study of delinquency.* On the basis of several years of collaboration with sociologists, a multidisciplinary approach has been worked out for the study of delinquency. We hope to continue our studies in delinquency with the patients referred to Bellevue from court and, possibly, to extend these studies to youngsters on probation in our community.

7. *Mental health needs of Spanish-speaking youngsters.* Initial efforts have been made to get a better idea of the problems confronting Puerto Ricans in New York City. This will give us a better idea of what to suggest concerning the mental health needs of Spanish-speaking children in our area.

This, in rough outline, was the training program I proposed for Bellevue two years ago. Except for full implementation of the research projects, it would essentially stand for the program currently in operation.

But the proposal I would make today is for a training program which will meet the needs of the residents as they step into practice two, three and especially five and ten years from now. The program I have read, quite acceptable by yesterday's standards, is obsolete for the psychiatry of tomorrow in a city such as New York.

First the training of residents, I believe, must be adjusted and adapted to the location in which the training is taking place. In New York City, therefore, the training should look beyond the confines of the hospital—in this case Bellevue—to utilize the sources and resources of the community which the hospital is designed to serve.

One may then develop a program which is truly relevant, to use the popular term of today, to the community, and thus to the resident, by offering service which would shape the training program. Rather than viewing service and training as somehow at odds and in conflict, I see them as totally compatible. If the training program that emerges from the service programs does not meet the needs and goals of any particular resident, he should find another adolescent training program that does. If this scheme were adopted, there would be many different training programs based on differing local conditions —and so every prospective trainee would find the program most suitable for him.

This does away with a universal training program in adolescent psychiatry, and in an age of ever-increasing specialization, means a number of different types of programs even within the already subdivided specialty of adolescent psychiatry.

In a big city hospital like Bellevue, the main emphasis has been on the inpatient services which have overshadowed the outpatient services. There are a number of historical and political reasons for this which need not be described here except to say that, as a matter of expediency, those who could not be maintained in the community necessarily had to be admitted and cared for, while those masses whose problems were somewhat less severe, so that on some level they could manage or at least survive, would be seen in the outpatient department on a voluntary basis. But such an attitude on the part of the big city hospital did little to endear itself to members of the community, which by and large had little good to say about the psychiatric services offered them.

The important point is that with a social revolution going

on all around us, psychiatry, of course, has been engulfed in it too. The use of drugs—of the tranquilizing variety—and the concept of community mental health programs have combined to shift the emphasis of treatment of very sick persons back to the home and community, rather than in remote areas away from the city where the state hospitals and residential treatment centers are situated.

In practice, if we can deliver the mental health services adolescents need, we cannot fail to deliver the training program the residents need. But for the training and service program to become relevant, dramatic changes must take place in the philosophy and attitudes of the administration of the hospital.

Before I discuss changes in the training program that would involve the community, I will outline the shifts in emphasis that I believe are needed even in basic clinical work and didactic courses.

And since I will be emphasizing throughout this discussion new and different approaches to the basic training program in adolescent psychiatry, I would like to pause here to make it very clear that I still believe in a solid traditional foundation for the training experience. No matter where we go from here, our trainees must still begin with a thorough understanding of individual psychopathology in terms of modern psychodynamic theories and treatment in one-to-one therapy. These remain the foundation upon which everything else is built.

Of the traditional modes of therapy, individual psychotherapy (short and long term, supportive and uncovering), psychopharmacotherapy (alone and combined with psychotherapy), and group and family therapy, these latter two are the newest and the ones to which more time should be devoted than is generally the case in current training programs for adolescent psychiatry.

In most institutions, because of pressure of time and lack of trained personnel, these two parts of the training program are slighted. They are, however, particularly appropriate modalities for the adolescent psychiatrist. The adolescent is particularly well suited to treatment in a group or family setting.

In this stage of development, joining groups is a natural phenomenon; it furthers the process by which youngsters find out more about themselves and others like themselves, and by which they gain strength and support on the road toward independence from parents. A natural group formation takes place, whether it be among boy scouts carrying badges or in gangs carrying knives. Either way the adolescent in a group is particularly open and touchable, whereas he might not be in individual therapy.

In a family therapy situation, the therapist is still doing group therapy, but of a special kind. The group involves the significant cast of characters who have contributed most powerfully to the adolescent's illness. Working with the adolescent without changing the pernicious family influences so often present is likely to prove futile.

Often the whole pattern of transaction among family members needs to be broken before the individual can be helped.

The extra dividends of these two modalities of treatment are, first, that, in both cases, one can offer help to more than one person at a time and second, that, especially in the family therapy situation, one has an excellent opportunity to employ preventive psychiatry for younger or future children.

I also believe that, as important new knowledge is gained in ancillary and related disciplines, such as anthropology and sociology, which have a direct bearing on psychiatry, this knowledge too should be incorporated in the training program.

More work in the community will necessarily require dealing with the cultural variables present in that locale. For the psychiatrist to evaluate correctly all the dynamics operating in a given pathological condition, he must be acquainted with anthropological and sociological concepts and integrate them into psychiatric theory.

This represents a major and crucial challenge; unless it is met, I believe the role of psychiatry in the mental health of the community will exert only a shadow of its potential force.

This brings us to the ways in which the training program can be fitted to the changing needs of the community. Although the hospital still operates as a home base, it should no longer be the only base of operations. The services and training should be done in various locales of the community—where the action is; where it is happening.

Residents should be rotated in other settings. This would include psychiatric consultation to the religious institutions in the neighborhood, operation of a store-front clinic in the areas, and offering help to the hippie youths, drug users, and runaways who would not come to a hospital facility, but who seek help in their own area.

The trainee would not merely evaluate the adolescents in trouble; he would work regularly with the personnel of institutions that deal with such youths, so that, for example, when going to the local public high school to see the adolescent who is referred by either the school psychologist or guidance counsellor or by a classroom teacher, the trainee would also hold a group session with teachers, training them to be more perceptive and understanding in their role as teachers.

Similarly, when going to juvenile court, the trainee would not only evaluate the delinquent, he would also have sessions with the probation officers, police, and even, though this might take more doing, the judges.

In cooperating with local religious institutions, the trainee would spend his allotted time not only interviewing youngsters in the religious setting, but also conducting advisory sessions with groups of ministers. This program would be designed to help the clergy work more effectively with their young parishioners. In all these endeavors, the trainees' work would be supervised by the senior staff. There are, I feel, many significant advantages in this kind of training: First, the scarcity of available psychiatrists who can treat individual adolescents means that only a fraction of the troubled youth population could possibly be helped by traditional means of therapy; second, seeing the youngsters in familiar and comfortable settings makes for quicker and easier rapport; third, referral by a neutral or hostile authority figure can be a key factor in determining whether or not treatment will be ultimately effective; fourth, the training program takes advantage of already on-going projects and programs so that, among other things, no extra financial burden is imposed on the hospital.

Finally, the trainee sees patients who would not come to the hospital—thus broadening and enriching his training experience. A notable example of a group of youngsters that I have found much more reachable for treatment if psychiatry set up shop on their turf is the so-called hippie community. For good or bad reasons, these youngsters, as well as others, may harbor deep resentment against authority, which they see in established institutions such as school, the courts, and the psychiatric hospitals. They will not voluntarily go to the hospital facility. Many members of this group have serious psychiatric disturbances and are in urgent need of help, yet such youngsters would not ordinarily be seen by the resident in his hospital setting. They are, however, readily approachable when seen in the area which represents security and home to them. The psychiatrist is showing respect, concern and other positive but intangible qualities when he goes into the hippie area to offer his help. As a group, these youngsters respond positively to this kind of interest.

In the East Village Project which is typical of the kind of set-up organized by a community group (in this case it was Jewish Family Services), the project consisted of a staff of eight social workers who saw one thousand youngsters last year; of these, over three hundred and fifty remained in some therapy program. They came to the East Village store, referred usually by a friend who had a kind word for the staff. The youngsters who came were runaways or emancipated minors with varying and sometimes intense need for psychiatric help.

The trainee would work in the store, evaluating the youngster seeking help, treating others, and then work with social workers in their therapeutic endeavors.

Such efforts to develop the skills of nonmedical professionals—teachers, probation officers, social workers, ministers and so on—means that they can be trained to take over more responsibility for offering therapy to adolescents in need. This kind of effort also involves tangible progress in the area that holds the most promise of any in our field—preventive psychiatry.

There is little disagreement among psychiatrists that the dynamics of psychopathology have their most important roots in intrafamilial relationships. However, unless the traumatic experiences here are of an overwhelming variety, salvage operations—or at least prevention of further deterioration—may be accomplished by one or another of the various adults whose contact with the youth can be a beneficial and therapeutic experience.

An example of a program where preventive psychiatry can be instituted is the sex education and family planning project which is being established by a second-year fellow in adolescent psychiatry.

In an area such as ours, where there is a high rate of pregnancy among unmarried teen-age girls, a program for sex education and family planning can be instituted either in a local church or school, or any available place where youngsters congregate and where they already have invested a trust and a faith. The psychiatric unit should take advantage of this, by joining forces in order to win a receptive and cooperative group of participants.

Another problem in urgent need of more effective programs is that of drug addiction among youths in New York and in our local catchment area. Addiction is increasing at an alarming rate, especially among the young.

The raging debate over the advantages of a methadone program versus a nondrug approach such as the therapeutic milieu of Synanon or Phoenix House is beside the point. The major problem confronting us is how to stop the explosion of our addict population.

A drug education program is by no means an adequate answer, but at least it is a start in the area. A resident can give a course in the schools where the problem is quite overt. Simple dissemination of facts can be of significant help. Open discussions can carry help a step further. Availability of friendly, knowledgeable adults may be useful when youngsters, experimenting with drugs, find it getting away from them and beyond their control.

To the extent that drug addiction, juvenile delinquency and other pathological conditions with sociocultural economic etiological factors have fallen into the domain of the psychiatrist, he must become more politically and socially active as a part of his training program—if he is to be effective. This means he must make some contact, either personally or through some emissary or other member of the team, with educational, housing, employment and other institutional representatives.

Unless the psychiatrist exerts his influence to change the unhealthy environmental conditions that contribute to many pathological states, the psychiatrist will become increasingly superfluous in the management of such important problems as drug addiction, juvenile delinquency, the hippie life-style. I stress these three because they are all widespread and *increasing,* and because in my personal experience, working in the ghetto areas of New York City, I have become convinced that one-to-one psychotherapy is not the best method of treatment for these problems. Furthermore, and perhaps most important, one-to-one psychotherapy in these cases does not address itself to prevention, which, in the long run, is the only effective answer.

The oft-cited complaint that the psychiatrist reaches too few persons in a professional lifetime to make this way of life the most useful is a valid one. There will always be a few persons who can pay for and benefit from individual therapy with a well-trained psychiatrist. And there will always be a few psychiatrists who find themselves most comfortable in doing such therapy. A combination of the right psychiatrist and patient will thus be effective even if it represents what will be an increasingly anachronistic mode of therapy.

Again, I should like to emphasize that the techniques of one-to-one therapy are by no means obsolete for today's training programs. Only through individual psychotherapy and supervision will the psychiatrist develop the deeper knowledge of the causes and treatments of personality disturbances. I would strongly urge my residents to have psychoanalytic training—but not with the idea that they would be doing private psychoanalysis for most of their working life. Rather, they should regard such training as clinical research (as well as therapy) and thus as a means of acquiring the best-known skills for understanding and treating mental illness. These skills can then be adapted to all the new programs in the community setting.

I believe the more typical role of the psychiatrist in the future is one in which he will use his knowledge of the development and treatment of mental illness to train others, sometimes in larger groups, who will be doing the treatment. At first this training would be given to members of paramedical disciplines, such as social workers, but later it would include other groups of indigenous workers whose basic relevant qualification for conducting therapy would be personal experience as a member of the group that needs help. Such a person, given normal intelligence and sensitivity, may be trained to do therapy with that group. An illustration I have in mind is the drug addict population in the lower east side of New York City.

The model for therapy is the addict who has been there and has been helped to find a way out. I am presently observing how a house of addicts run by a staff of ex-addicts under the supervision of a psychiatrist is achieving very promising results. In the encounter sessions, the ex-addict runs the group better than any group psychotherapist could.

You may not have to be one to cure one—but it helps—providing you have found answers that work.

This is the second large group of persons to be trained to do therapy—persons indigenous to the community, who know the people and who are readily admitted into their homes and lives. From this group, persons with ability to work with others can be formally trained and supervised by the psychiatrist, whose general skills can be effectively adapted for their use.

The goals can be as limited as symptom removal, or as ambitious as profound characterological change.

The psychiatrist's future work very likely will be conducted as part of a team approach toward curing many of the social ills which increasingly compromise day to day living. He will teach and supervise groups of workers who in turn will handle the daily treatment. He will apply his knowledge—both psychiatric and psychoanalytic—in the training of others. He will be administratively involved in institutional policies, contributing to policy-making on every level—from deciding co-ed visiting hours in college dormitories to recommending changes in ghetto life that will help eliminate drug addiction and delinquency.

Chapter Five

Education of Psychiatrists for College Practice

MERTON J. KAHNE

IN THIS PAPER I wish to place before you a series of perspectives on the education of psychiatrists which has guided the development of our fellowship program at the Massachusetts Institute of Technology. As may be anticipated from the title of this paper, I have quite deliberately exercised the prerogative of a social scientist and psychiatrist to redefine the nature of the problem along lines congruent with a mode of conceptualization which we have found increasingly useful in our attempts to come to grips with providing the specialized education which we now believe necessary for effective psychiatric practice in the contemporary American college.

To begin with, it will be noted that I have quite deliberately avoided describing our program as centrally focused on students. Our service is not a student mental health station but is, we hope, moving towards becoming a community psychiatric resource. We are open to faculty, administrative personnel, blue-collar workers and the families and friends of all of these. Our charter permits us, in emergencies, to see any individual who bears a logical or social relationship to any member of the MIT community, irrespective of his formal affiliation with MIT.

But, although I wish to focus on the environmental dimensions of the problem, I shall not attempt to give a complete description of our program, but will attempt to center my remarks around those educational issues particularly influenced by the fact that a large part of our clientele are late adolescent students. We are certainly mindful of the importance of developing in our psychiatric fellows detailed understanding of the phenomenology and characteristic developmental tasks of late adolescence in such a fashion as to permit them to engage students who come under their care in a meaningful fashion. However, it has been our experience that the most critical educational task facing us has been in generating, in the psychiatric practitioner, a full appreciation of the significance of the college environment in promoting or interfering with the student's short-term and long-term, psychological, intellectual and social adaptation. For some time now, it has been clear to us that if we would do more than pay lip service to the contributions of our social science colleagues to the understanding of human behavior, that we must redesign the entire encounter with potential patients in such a fashion as to make it necessary for the psychiatrist to assess routinely the contribution of the patient's social environment to the problem as experienced by the patient, and to *negotiate* with the patient a meaningful set of *mutually shared* assumptions about the social meaning to be attributed to their interchange.

I want to emphasize this redefinition of the service objectives, precisely because what is at issue here in the education of psychiatrists is the question of whether or not it is legitimate to assume that the psychology of an individual may be reliably conceptualized in a fashion which permits effective social psychological intervention into his life without a detailed knowledge of his particular environment. In our view, it is not possible for the psychiatrist to understand the student's perspective unless he has a quite intimate knowledge of the community within which the student's experience is being formed.

What is also at issue, and this does relate quite specifically to the special problems associated with any attempt to be of use to late adolescent or early adult patients, is the feasibility of restructuring the concept of the psychiatrist's role so as to include the possibility of engagement of individuals under circumstances that are conceptualized by them as stressful but not necessarily pathological.

Much of adolescent crisis and turmoil is transitory. Many students who have seemingly formidable problems during college are basically healthy adolescents who, given reasonable opportunity to do so, can work through their surging conflicts and eventually come to assume their roles as mature, healthy adults. Considered from this point of view, strategies of assistance which do not presume involved long-term psychological commitment become feasible conceptual bases for planning formal institutional support programs. A minimum of timely short-term counseling or other intervention often serves to minimize the more overwhelming transient social and psychological pressures impinging on a student and helps him to sort out the more relevant issues for his progressive mastery of life.

At the same time, the effectiveness of such programs depends on one's ability to differentiate quickly problems and situations which, by and large, lend themselves to minimal, though important, involvement on the part of a counsellor from those less likely to be resolved without the more time-consuming or formally structured "therapeutic" programs. Such differentiation, in our view, requires more than an expert grasp of individual psychopathology as it is generally conceived. One needs at least to know something about the student's perception of his condition, its historical circumstances, the attitudinal influences on the student, the likelihood that a college caretaker might even become aware that his skills and services are needed, the social facilities available, and finally the most appropriate avenues for effecting a meaningful and useful contact.

We know, for example, that at MIT, academic problems, crises of identity, conflict in deciding on a professional career, problems in heterosexual adjustment, interpersonal difficulties with peers, the draft, and financial problems account for about 85 percent of the reasons given by the students for consulting the psychiatrist. As problems, they are not much different from the concerns of college students in general.[7] And certainly they contain within them all of what has come to be known in psychological circles as the developmental tasks of adolescence. But identity crises have qualitatively different dimensions at MIT than elsewhere.[12] Snyder summarized inferences drawn from interviews with students conducted by him for the MIT Student Adaptation Study as follows:

> Students all stress their association with MIT as meaning that they were at the "best" college where the "best" brains in the country are there to teach them. They appear to think of other colleges as second-class. This belief contributes to a student's vulnerability to depression if he becomes aware that he is not achieving or producing well enough. The usual MIT student came from the top 6 percent of his high school graduating class, but after entering MIT most of these students had to fill the ranks of the bottom 95 percent of their class. Despite their intellectual awareness of the inevitability of this, it nevertheless was experienced as a severe emotional shock to most students when it actually occurred, and this shock combined with the tendency for many MIT students to think in either/or terms, commonly brought them to the deduction that if they were not at the top of the class, they must be among the worst students in the class.

This quotation should not be regarded as an exercise in academic chauvinism. It is chosen quite deliberately to focus on the importance of the psychiatrist understanding the detailed meaning of events which are rather simply labelled "identity crises." Other institutions, no doubt, can provide their own analogies. What is distinctive at MIT at its present stage of development is that it is primarily addressing itself to the education of technological elites and that this fact has special consequences when one finds oneself attempting to understand and be of assistance to students with the above problems. A student's decision to alter his professional career more often than not is really a forced choice occurring under circumstances where the event is socially conceived of as an actual failure. For example: certain otherwise very competent students of physics quite abruptly discover that they cannot master the requirements of quantum mechanics because of an inability to comprehend relations between objects under study without recourse to a visual model. In quantum mechanics there is, at present, a severe handicap often resulting in a forced decision by students to change their career line. This crisis in identity is usually accompanied by severe loss of self esteem—an alteration in attitude towards self which unfortunately usually becomes permanent unless dealt with at the time of transformation. Also, students wishing to exercise legitimate options to secure draft deferment must be especially careful lest they compromise their possibility of working on highly technical problems in physics, engineering and mathematics available only in federally sponsored programs. Even the traditional difficulties in heterosexual adjustment are complicated by quite specific social traditions which effectively delineate the range of choices and the conditions for success in making a date. Success or failure in academic matters is heavily dependent on the student's ability selectively to neglect certain of the prescribed courses, or particular activities and studies within a course, in the interests of simple academic survival. And for a large portion of students and faculty alike, the characterological urge to find out, to be in control of, and to have a conscious sense of mastery of one's physical world exercises a most important influence on their style of life. Among MIT students an unwritten code which stresses independence from adult help and places emphasis on working out one's own problems compromises simple acceptance of formal college counseling resources.

In the interest of becoming an effective resource, we have had to go into the classroom and dormitory and engage students directly in nonclinical situations. In the process we have begun to learn something about the social genesis of a good deal of the somewhat exaggerated preoccupation with control and independence. As will be noted later, educational styles and educational traditions which can readily be observed in classroom transactions quickly communicate to the student that he risks humiliation, criticism, and ridicule through naive self-exposure. We contend then that an appreciation of this community cannot be gained by hearsay, intellectual discussion, or experience vicariously gained through the reports of the patients. The psychiatrist, we believe, needs concrete experience in dealing with deans, the professors, the administrative personnel and the friends and associates with whom the student is currently engaged.

In a recent article, we have asserted that a psychiatric service in the college environment, if it is fully to engage the social problems which may be found there, needs to be "something more than simply a facility for the treatment of mental illness." At its best it "appears to function more like a clearinghouse where individuals with vaguely defined, often contradictory social perceptions, can find an informed neutral arena where time is made available for examination and clarification of the issues."[13] Such a conception constitutes, for many psychiatrists, too radical a departure from the more classical medical models to which they have become accustomed. Given the fact that the process of psychiatric training as it is presently structured provides little opportunity for psychiatric residents to work regularly with people who conceive of themselves as normal, there are relatively few psychiatrists who can adapt themselves to the altered relationships without experiencing considerable strain.

Nowhere, across the entire spectrum of psychiatric practice, are the untoward consequences of initiating psychiatric resident training in mental hospitals more devastating than they are in college work. Psychiatrists accustomed to rough and ready rule-of-thumb diagnoses of schizophrenia based on reported oddities of perception, peculiarity of speech, and strongly held unusual ideas, can wreak havoc in an encounter with imaginative college students. Practitioners, accustomed to authority developed in settings of primitive coercion and constraint and neatly scheduled appointment hours, will find themselves frustrated and perplexed and all too quickly vindictively demeaning of students when they find themselves as much inquired about, as inquiring into the lives of others; as much interrupted in their daily routines as they are customarily disruptive of the ordinary affairs of their patients.

A psychiatric fellow's retreat into obsessional preoccupation with the strength of the *patient's ego* to deal with life events is but one of a series of readily recognized indications to us that we have probably lost our battle to promote understanding.

Another area requiring extensive re-education for the would-be college psychiatrist is the legitimacy of advice-giving and of providing himself as a real object for relatedness among students. For many reasons, the process is distinctly different from the kind of relatedness psychiatrists working in mental institutions or medical outpatient departments develop with their patients. To begin with, in the college environment the psychiatrist is but one of a large number of potential authority figures and except in unusual circumstances, he is *not* the most important individual in the student's life. Secondly, a student turning to the psychiatrist for help is usually simultaneously exploring other resources available to him, such as the deans or tutorial assistants, as well as student friends. And many quite deliberately evaluate the relative merits of the advice they receive from the various resources. The psychiatrist accustomed to being the central architect of a remedial plan, having to compete in the marketplace of ideas with others and finding repeatedly that many of his recommendations for action are not in fact followed through, frequently finds the process difficult to take. Furthermore, in most instances, a major objective in the psychiatrist/student relationship is promoting the student's gaining of experience in decision-making based on the requirements of the situation as he formulates it—rather than on the basis of the "received wisdom" of others. Psychiatrists who find it necessary to promote dependence on themselves will find work with students filled with conflict and contradiction.

Another aspect of work with students which frequently causes consternation to the psychiatrist is the much wider range of assumptions the students make about the meaning of a personal relationship than does the adult psychiatrist. While most students expect fidelity and honesty in their negotiations with the psychiatrist, and certainly expect their encounter to be treated as a privileged communication, their lack of sophistication about, and indifference to, the complexity of professional relationships leads them at times to be exasperatingly demanding when the logic of the situation for them requires that the psychiatrist behave in a fashion which he would himself ordinarily regard as violation of professional ethics or legal jurisdiction. Students have great difficulty in accepting the professional's inability to act without authority and are impatient with "techniques."

In many respects the psychiatrist in the college must also master methods and practices familiar to a sophisticated psychiatric social worker. Recognizing the value of the telephone and brief letters or notes and the importance of actively seeking out and following through the arrangement of conferences among parties to a dispute or disturbed relationship, and developing the capacity to function as a public figure while at the same time retaining enough reserve so as to be useful therapeutically to students, are talents the mastery of which requires considerable discussion and guidance.

Deliberately structuring the process of engagement along lines that are conceived of as within a normal range by both the student and the psychiatrist, permits the psychiatrist to gain insight into the way in which contemporary processes of education provide a substantial basis for the young adolescent to forego many of the struggles so characteristic of the adolescent condition. We have become most sensitive to one undesirable adaptation. Some students, in attempting to develop a strategy of educational "success" adopt patterns of engagement which effectively limit the possibility of continued intellectual and emotional growth. In structuring their relations with instructors and peers so as to make themselevs relatively impervious to professional criticism they also limit the full development of their initial potentialities. They mimic and quickly incorporate the style and attitudes of their most feared teachers. In psychoanalytic terms, identification with the aggressor is a process which quite commonly may be observed to be appearing among students in response to the daily behavior of professors, instructors, and teaching assistants. In professional schools this process, when it occurs, is especially vicious because the various individuals involved are locked into the same social process and are at different stages of internalization of the model. Anyone who has sat through one semester in a classroom can readily observe the caricatures and mimicry as these students begin to adopt a style of behavior which eventually distinguishes one professional group from another. The instructors can be observed to be apeing the professors, teaching assistants adopting the style of their instructors, etc.

I have focused attention on the notion of identification with the aggressor advisedly, because while in truth one still finds models for student identification that are much more benign and benevolent in their effect on students, the sad fact is that much of what passes for contemporary educational behavior in the American classroom consists of ritualized *rites de passage* where the threat of humiliation constantly hangs over the pursuit of knowledge.

Our fellowship program has been designed so as to create a very close interpenetration of the ideas and insights emerging in clinical situations with the concepts and assumptions of our Educational Research Center. This, together with carefully developed and jealously guarded mutual trust between ourselves and our faculty and administration, has made it possible to structure research inquiries into the educational scene which provide unambiguous data to the effect that even in circumstances of conscientious faculty attempts to promote an exciting educational environment, serious perversions of adequate social process occur. We also know, for example, that certain repetitious situational stresses characteristic of a particular academic course create strain in students and faculty at different points in the academic year and at different stages in the career development of students.[8,9,10] We know, furthermore, that it makes a difference whether or not a student consults our psychiatric service before or after a contemplated residence change—in terms of the probability of his remaining in college.[14] That such processes eventually contribute to something more than disagreeable situations to be endured, is suggested by the gross similarity between some of the processes which we have been able to observe and record, and the conditions for successful debasement of personality and discrediting of identity described by Goffman[5,6] and others, in, for example, the mental hospital.

We contend that any psychiatrist who would attempt to work with the students must become sensitized to the reality of these events as a commonplace, and gain experience in developing effective strategies for protecting his patients from the worst excesses of the present practices. He must also gain skill in educating educators to the implications of his findings for preventive social psychiatric purposes. For example, at the conclusion of one of our studies of the social structure of a major discipline I was asked to report my "findings and recommendations" to the entire faculty—a group numbering well over three hundred members. I declined. Instead, I offered to meet for extended lunch dialogues with the faculty in groups of no more than twenty-five people. At these meetings I presented my observations, stated my thesis about what I thought constituted a desirable educational process and defended the inferences I drew from my observations in active interchange with faculty. I offered no prescriptions for change but encouraged faculty to discuss whether they agreed with my observations and to elaborate their own educational perspectives. This process, while time consuming, was, we think, crucial to making our research socially meaningful. Not only did it create the possibility for fuller collaboration between ourselves and the faculty, but it also permitted us to check the adequacies of our constructs in the ensuing discussions; it permitted the faculty to confront each other with previously inexplicit differences in perspective (occasionally a previously unrecognized consensus would emerge) and provided a spur towards *faculty initiated* reform. Most importantly, it prevented our work from falling into the sterile limbo of "outsider research," which pads the curriculum vitae of academic aspirants but never engages the participants to the events.

We expect then, that our fellows will, in addition to clinical work, systematically engage in becoming familiar with actual classroom practices and will in the course of their education learn how to evaluate and influence the social climate of the college in which they eventually come to work. Through work with committees on educational policy, committees on academic performance and the like, we anticipate that they will come to appreciate the complexity of student-faculty relations. In the process, we expect that they will eventually begin to develop techniques of negotiation with some participants *which do not* initially depend upon trust. The trusting relationship, so crucial to successful engagement of classical psychiatric patients, is not in our view sufficient to the needs which we expect to meet in our community. In the present state of our development we conceive of techniques commonly employed by labor relations arbitrators as perhaps useful in bringing together individuals who do not necessarily have common objectives or common perspectives on a given situation.

For the young psychiatrist, whose education and practice has thus far been confined largely to medical clinics and mental hospitals, a considerable amount of unlearning must take place. In encounters characterized by initial distrust, recourse to the more conventional techniques of establishing professional authority leads quite quickly to a student's disengagement and to rapid disaccreditation of the psychiatrist in the institutional grapevine. Since our students constitute the most important influence on another student in forming an opinion,[11] the psychiatrist's first clinical encounter biases the student's evaluation of him somewhat excessively. We therefore have gone to great pains to supervise these initial clinical encounters with student patients with especially experienced therapists.

As part of his education, the psychiatrist is also asked to engage students in situations outside of the clinic, in dormitories, social clubs and various other extracurricular associations. While some of this is undertaken because discussions with students will be a common part of the psychiatrist's participation in the university life,* 1 we make it quite clear to the student psychiatrist that it is of considerable importance that he engage students in their everyday activities so as to familiarize himself with the wide variety of performances and behaviors that constitute the norm of student existence. Psychiatrists accustomed to dealing with individuals who have previously identified themselves as ill are usually unprepared for the phenomena commonly encountered in conversations with many normal adolescents. While many of them have read poignant descriptions of adolescent behavior, it is a rare psychiatrist indeed who can avoid retreat into labelling.

We have found that not only have our attempts to normalize the social situation in which students and psychiatrist encounter each other proved useful in terms of increasing their "therapeutic" effectiveness, but also the insights gained from a studied attempt to trace out the intimate relations between contemporary stress situations, life situations, and organizational structure have greatly enriched our understanding of the social sources of the contemporary student's disenchantment with the current American educational institutions. For example, college educators in America are commonly seen as having as one of their responsibilities the establishment of an environment believed to facilitate students' potential for establishing a sense of self, sexual preference, social and occupa-

---

* In some sense we have been trying to institutionalize, both in our clinic practice and in our fellows program, what Ackerly has described as his role as Psychiatrist-in-Residence at the University of Louisville in 1963. This author presents a rather dramatic description of himself as a catalytic agent whose function it was to stimulate an interplay of ideas among students and between students and faculty. Actually the paper is a composite account in dialogue form of conversations with college students who come to him *not as patients* but on their own—"hungry to talk." Our approach differs somewhat in that for the most part the content of our dialogue with students is usually considerably more mundane. We also expect that the psychiatrist as well as the student will be changed by the exchange. The concept of psychiatrist-as-catalyst is alien to our thinking whether in the brief encounters or formal therapy.

tional career, and an increasing abandonment of childhood dependence on parents in negotiating problems in living. However, inherent in the system there exist many equally important practices which usually act as deterrents to the realization of these objectives. In limiting and selecting the nature and sequence of the traditional educational content in the interest of *guiding* the student along paths which it is believed will better equip him to understand the world in which he lives, and in requiring him formally to identify his career interests early, educators often promote and prolong dependence and frustrate the stabilization of the student's identity.[2] And, in establishing standardized rules and regulations as, for example, those associated with dormitory living, there are created the grossest distortions of ordinary emerging sexual relationships. Furthermore, the advanced degree system not only perpetuates a student's dependence, but as Erikson points out, the trend toward liberal arts education puts off "getting the tools of technology of one's chosen career for a preoccupation with refined 'literacy.' "[3]

But promoting more normal social interchanges among psychiatrists and students, while necessary, is not sufficient to promote real engagement around important issues. We find it of considerable importance for our staff and fellows to schedule seminars and discussions dealing with social problems which currently occupy much of our students' concern. Thus we regularly expose ourselves to the opinions and ideas of city planners, civil rights workers, politicians, pushers and users of drugs, radical students, lawyers, T-group operators, Vista workers, etc. Achieving and maintaining relevance for students requires nothing more nor less than making an active attempt to remain informed about that which matters to them.*

---

* Parenthetically, it is by common consensus the fact of the opportunity to engage these issues actively and repetitively, both in our academic conferences and with students and others, that attracts our staff to what is otherwise often very demanding work. Usually it is experienced as an invigorating chance to maintain a diversity of interests and to keep in touch with what is going on in the world.

To further insure the reality of our psychiatric fellows confronting themselves with the necessity to master the sociology of the college student's experience, we have created the possibility of educating nonpsychiatric fellows in association with our psychiatrists. Our program explicitly provides for the possibility of educating postdoctoral engineers, architects, city planners, sociologists and the like, who for obvious reasons are interested in clinical, social-psychological perspectives on the systems of human relations which they expect to engage in their professional work. Currently, for example, one of our fellows is an architect in the department of city planning who is a trained anthropologist interested in college environments. He is pursuing a set of studies aimed at clarifying the political issues entering into a decision to construct a particular campus building. Through regular interchanges with the psychiatric personnel we hope to promote an increasingly intimate and fruitful dialogue at a stage in the development of our postdoctoral fellows where the constraints of professionalization have not yet exercised their fully crippling effect, and where one may hope for reasonable breakthroughs in conceptual formulations which might eventually get us out of the morass of contradiction and misplaced emphasis in social planning in which we now often find ourselves.

In this discussion, I have quite deliberately not addressed myself to the very real and vexing problems of educating psychiatrists in effective methods for working with students who use drugs, assisting pregnant students, and engaging the complex social psychology that constitutes what has euphemistically been called "student unrest." There can be no doubt that each of these areas reaches to the roots of student existence and challenges all of our concepts about what late adolescence is all about. It seems to us that for problems such as these, none of us can lay claim to any special expertise. We therefore go to great pains not to confuse our trainees with misguided illusions of special knowledge. Certainly there is more than ample room for skepticism regarding the adequacy of our understanding of the drug experience in the lives of adolescents. Most of us have learned to speak less glibly about what formerly were regarded as the almost inevitable psychological consequences of abortion. And surely the reality of the contemporary American college faculty abdication of its educational responsibilities cannot be dismissed by focusing on the social and demographic characteristics of campus radical leaders. On issues such as these, we are all unquestionably naive. It is our hope that in creating as open a situation as possible between our students and ourselves, we may be able to foster the mutual trust and respect which appears to be a precondition for the emergence of the empathy necessary to insight.

Nor do we burden our trainees with false expectations that we have worked out any especially effective, intellectually defensible methods for the provision of definitive care of patients with well established neuroses. Like psychiatric administrators everywhere, we limp along, doing the best we can with limited economic resources, scarcity of talent, and conflicting theories of the most effective treatment programs to promote for given difficulties.

But we do encourage experimentation and encourage staff and fellows alike in making their plans for intervention explicit, fleshing out the social psychological assumptions on which the plans are based, the nature of the expected outcome, and eventually reporting back to the group on what, in fact, did happen. And we also support the development of tailor-made social structures designed to address themselves to our particular clientele. Most recently, for example, we have begun to bring into being a day care facility specially designed to meet the needs of students.* Another program which we are developing is a time-limited group which comprises students and others who are leaving the Institute for whom we have reason to believe the process of separation will be especially

---

* At MIT this probably means eventual incorporation of a terminal for access to a time-shared computer in intimate juxtaposition to the standard "therapeutic" adjuvants—the coffeepot and the guitar and the standard paraphernalia necessary to cast an accurate horoscope!

trying. We also are making extended efforts continuously to evaluate the effectiveness of our interventions—capitalizing on the fact that it is not too hard to locate students via the college grapevine.

Our fellows have the possibility of taking formal academic courses at the Institute, or if they have the talent and inclination, of structuring a social psychiatric research inquiry. These activities are planned individually with the trainee—they are not routine nor are they completely at the fellows' option. To avoid the deterioration of this phase of their education into ritualistic performance, each fellow must negotiate the conditions and nature of his special proposal. By the same token, the psychiatrist is not *automatically* assigned to any class of clinical activity. Each phase of his work is monitored by an experienced advisor and his next activity planned with him in accordance with a consensus about his evolving competence.

Developing, and successfully executing, postgraduate education of this type is exquisitely dependent on the talents, interests, concerns and energy of the clinical staff. None of our fellows are novices to the general clinical practice of psychiatry. The special experience, intuition, and tact required for the re-education of colleagues cannot be achieved by administrative fiat. Nor can such a program be engrafted as an addendum to the work of a group of practitioners who no longer regard the encounters of clinical practice as problematical. Like the best of the educators in whose midst they work, one notices among the staff an inventiveness and an urge to share professional experiences which is infectious, and one experiences a seductive invitation to live with controversy, complexity, and ambiguity in the interests of satisfying one's curiosity.

Finally, in negotiating the conditions of his education with the psychiatric fellow, we quite clearly are attempting to practice what we preach. By establishing the reality of our point of view in our work with him we hope he will adopt it as his own in his work with the people he encounters as a college psychiatrist. While our model for interpersonal transaction is especially important for the engagement of post-adolescent students because of the well-known self-consciousness that attends their reformulation of their identity, we are convinced of its equal applicability for guiding the fellow's transformation of identity, a process which, we believe, must attend any successful education.

REFERENCES

1. Ackerly, Spafford: A broad approach in college mental health. *Behav Neuropsychiat, 1*:3, 1969.
2. Berger, Bennett: Adolescence and beyond. *Social Problems, 10*: 394–408, 1963.
3. Erikson, Erik: Late adolescence. In Funkenstein, Daniel (Ed.): *The Student and Mental Health, An International View.* Cambridge, Riverside, 1959, p. 86.
4. Farnsworth, D. L.: *Psychiatry, Education and The Young Adult.* Springfield, Thomas, 1966.
5. Goffman, Erving: *Asylums.* New York, Doubleday, 1961.
6. Goffman, Erving: Stigma. *Notes on the Management of Spoiled Identity.* New Jersey, Prentice Hall, 1963.
7. The Harris Survey, *Washington Post,* March 18, 1965, p. d-1.
8. Kahne, M. J.: Psychiatric observer in the classroom. *Medical Trial Technique Quarterly,* June, 1969, pp. 81–98.
9. Parlett, Malcolm: Classroom and beyond. Educational Research Center, Massachusetts Institute of Technology, 1967.
10. Parlett, Malcolm, and King, John G.: Concentrated study. Occasional papers of the Educational Research Center, the Massachusetts Institute of Technology, 1969.
11. Presma, Donna: An exploratory study of the major problems experienced by undergraduate students and of the factors that may influence their use of counselling resources. Thesis submitted in partial fulfillment of requirements for the M.S.W. Degree, Smith College School for Social Work, 1968.
12. Snyder, Benson R.: Report on Massachusetts Institute of Technology Student Adaptation Study. Educational Research Center, Massachusetts Institute of Technology, Cambridge, Mass., 1967.
13. Snyder, Benson R., and Kahne, Merton J.: Stress in higher education and student use of university psychiatrists. *Amer J Orthopsychiat, 39* (1):34, 1969.
14. Taylor, James: A comparison of academic and non-academic variables in three MIT living groups. Thesis submitted in partial fulfillment of requirements for the M.S. Degree, MIT, 1967.

Section III

FAMILY THERAPY:
ONE TYPE OF INTERVENTION

Chapter Six

Reconceptualization of Adolescent Dynamics from the Family Point of View*

Salvador Minuchin

A CHILD'S BEHAVIOR is caused by many factors. Some are "inside" the child, like neurons, brains, and glands, as well as memories, motivations, introjects and drives. "Outside" the child are factors like his parents, his siblings, his family's socioeconomic status, his house, his school (teacher, peers and curriculum), his neighborhood, his neighborhood peer group, the hue of his skin, television and many others.

The major theoretical systems in child psychiatry have always been concerned with the influence of both internal and external factors on the development of the child. Particular emphasis has been put, in theory, on the biological and psychological needs, and what negotiates those needs within the nurturing and socializing unit called the family.

But the techniques of intervention which have been developed by child psychiatry have been aimed almost entirely at the child as a separate organism. Though the *theories* subscribed to have taken account of the importance of external factors in the child's development, the techniques used to change the child have not. Therefore, the context of interventions has been psychiatrist plus child.

This approach to therapy requires an awareness of only two people. The context of the intervention is not recognized as important; the behavior of the child in the therapy session is assumed to be typical of his usual behavior and somehow unaffected by his strange surroundings. The therapist and

---

* Reprinted from Anthony & Koupernik (Eds.), *The Child in His Family*. New York, John Wiley & Sons, 1970. (By Permission)

the child are involved in transactions in a new and perhaps frightening situation for the child in which the therapist nevertheless perceives himself as an observer-participant.

Family therapy, with its wider focus, has not been accepted by child psychiatry in the United States. Perhaps this is because family intervention requires a theory that can encompass at least three people, constantly involved in transactions with one another. The theory also must take into account the processes which constantly occur "across the boundaries" between family members, family subunits, and between the family and significant extrafamilial influences.

The focus of family therapy is necessarily wider than that of traditional child psychiatry, but even family therapy has tended to limit its interventions to the family, without extending its fields of intervention to the school, the neighborhood, or in some cases, even the extended family.[23]

Now these traditional concepts of the explanation of behavioral phenomena and techniques for intervention are being challenged by a combination of new theoretical systems such as general systems theory,[30] communications,[32] group dynamics,[7,31] and ecology,[4,5,6] and new techniques of intervention which stem from family therapy,[1,10,13,14,19,21,23,27,33,34,35] encounter groups,[3,24,28] and community psychiatry.[2,17,24,26]

The work of Roger G. Barker,[4,5,6] who has studied child behavior as affected by the different contexts of various natural settings, is an example of approaches which can be used as steps towards a more inclusive theory of behavior and change-producing intervention. Barker, a psychologist, writes:[4]

> The psychological person who writes essays, scores points, and crosses streets stands as an identifiable entity between unstable interior parts and exterior contexts, with both of which he is linked, yet from both of which he is profoundly separated. The separation comes from the fact that the inside parts and the outside contexts of a person involve phenomena that function according to laws that are different from those that govern his behavior.

In other words, to study the child, three elements must be studied independently. One is the child as an individual;

another is the environment in which his behavior is observed; third, is the linkage between these two elements. What processes are occurring across the boundaries which separate the individual child from his environment, and what is the nature of the mutual impingement of child and environment which is occurring?

Here is a key to one of the problems which have handicapped the development of a more inclusive intervention system in psychiatry. Psychiatry has been concerned with the development of a unified science. It has approached extra-individual units with the assumption that somehow the laws of group dynamics ought to be similar to the laws governing individual dynamics. The concept of the "undifferentiated family ego mass"[9] and the concepts of multiple transference used by some group therapists and family therapists[15] are examples of attempts to stretch individual concepts and adapt them to use with nonindividual theories and techniques.[21] This attempt to extend concepts developed for one theoretical context to use with another may well be inappropriate.

Barker's metaphor is helpful here.[4] He pictures a freight train crossing the plains of the Midwest, carrying wheat to Chicago. The laws which govern the growth of wheat are quite separate from those which govern the motion of the train. The laws which govern the motion of the train are quite different from those which will regulate the price of the wheat, and so on. Each of these are separate areas, which can be studied separately according to separate conceptualizations. But the market analyst who wants to predict the cost of flour may well have to take all of them into account.

The child psychiatrist operating within an ecological framework is in the position of that market analyst. He can study his patient in different contexts, determining the significance of those contexts and their relationship to each other. Then he can determine where and how intervention will be maximally effective.

For the ecological psychiatrist working with children, the child's family will usually be the most significant area for intervention, although the school, peers, neighborhood, and others may sometimes be as significant.

In his terms, the family is a behavioral setting which comprises the child.* From this point of view, the family is an extraindividual unit with regulatory power over the behavior of its members. At the same time, each member of the family has a separate identity; he is an individual as well as an interacting member of the family unit. The members of a family will exhibit the characteristic pattern of behavior which pertains to that family. At the same time, all the family members will compass the family rules in their own individual, differentiated ways.

The B family (which will be discussed later in this paper) is a good example of the regulatory power of a family unit. The B's are very much upper-class, respectable, proper Quakers. They pride themselves on the absence of disagreement in their family life, treasuring a seemly consensus in their family functioning. They have also firmly incorporated the philosophy of reverence for life. When the older son reached adolescence and began to disagree with his father, the family rules made it impossible for him to disagree openly. So he remained a respectful obedient child while developing a syndrome of *anorexia nervosa*, not eating because he maintained that eating destroys life.

The child and the family, then, are systems with properties of their own, each closely interrelated with the other. The same is true for subunits of the family such as the spouse or the sibling group. The separate subunits have their own structure and dynamics, and at the same time they are interdependent with the family and larger surrounding systems. Though all these systems may be operating independently at their own levels, they still have strong linkages across their system boundaries. And the boundaries of every system are more or less permeable, depending upon the system and the surrounding circumstances.

---

* I am indebted to Barker[4] for his discussion of behavioral settings, which I have adapted here for the discussion of the family.

The family as a system has standing patterns, programs, and goals. It also has ways of communicating and interacting which maintain these programs and goals. Whenever the family's accustomed methods of interaction are threatened by extrafamilial forces or the deviation of a family member, the family network is activated to preserve the usual equilibrium.

At the same time, the family system is responding to pressures from the individual members. For example, when a child enters adolescence and has to adapt both to his family and to an increasingly important peer group, he exerts pressure for more autonomy. If the family is to continue as a healthy, growth-encouraging unit, it must evolve from the family of a young child to the family of an adolescent. It was the inability of the B family to make this kind of adjustment that resulted in the appearance of pathology in its older son. But ordinarily, there will be extensive adjustments in areas of regulation and control, and the family's regulatory system will consequently change.

The concept of ecological psychiatry can take the many different factors influencing a child's development into account. And as in Barker's metaphor of the train, the different areas of significance can be analyzed without any demand that the laws governing them be conceptualized as somehow interrelated. Studies of the child's level of free fatty acid when subjected to specific stresses, studies of memory, perception, motivations, introjects, and so on, are potentially useful to the broad systems approach. And other studies, such as studies of the family system, will clearly be relevant. Families with engaged and disengaged characteristics may be studied in terms of the regulation of family members and the network for the development of controls. Large families and families with only children can be studied along this variable. The different social nets of families in small towns, slums, and kibbutzim can be studied from the point of view of the linkage between context and family (which hitherto has been the concern of sociology), and the relationship of the family members via intrapsychic linkages (which has hitherto been the field of psychologists and psychiatrists). Studies of this sort will add greatly to our understanding of individual and family dynamics, and within the concept of ecological psychiatry, there is no demand that the *studies* necessarily be related to one another.

In terms of therapeutic *intervention*, however, connections must be made. This will necessitate the study of the links which connect the child and his family, the family and the school, the family and the neighborhood, and so on.

It is in terms of change-producing interventions that the ecological framework indicates changes in the field of child psychiatry. Traditional child psychiatry has operated with the assumption that successful therapeutic intervention within the behavioral setting which comprises psychiatrist and child will produce changes in the intrapsychic life of the child. These changes will, in turn, ensure changes in his relationships with his ecology. The ecological framework challenges this assumption, and a number of corollaries which have accompanied it are also brought under review.

One corollary is a lack of understanding or concern about the influences of the contexts of behavior. The assumption has been that if the psychiatrist observes the child at play in a dyadic interaction with the psychiatrist himself, he is observing a sample of the child's typical behavior. The psychiatrist usually assumes that he is functioning only as a recorder of the child's behavior.

But from an ecological point of view, the therapist is seen as a manipulator as well as an observer and recorder. In other words, he must be influencing the child's behavior even if he is only recording it. In fact, usually he actually dominates the system of transactions between himself and the child because he provides and regulates input.

Another corollary which is challenged is the notion that one can intervene with the child alone. Because the child is a member of ecological settings other than the therapist-child, the therapist's interventions with the child will resound in these other settings, whether the therapist intends this or not. And the results of his interventions with the child may produce counterreactions that will have profound effect on the therapeutic task.

These challenges to traditional child psychiatry operate at the same time to the advantage of the child psychiatrist because a realization of the importance of the child's ecology opens new avenues of intervention. Because he recognizes that interventions with the child will have effects on his significant surrounding systems, and vice versa, the therapist is no longer limited to intervening with the child alone. He can intervene with the family, the neighborhood peer group, the school, and many other parts of the child's ecosystem, and thus reach the child from many different points of approach.

I would like to illustrate the advantage of an ecological approach to a child by presenting the B case. This family came to our attention because the oldest son, Stephen, aged fifteen, had developed eating fads so restrictive that in the last three months he had lost thirty pounds, or about 25 percent of his body weight. He had become a vegetarian a year before on the grounds of reverence for life, and had gradually cut out more and more foods. Now he was eating only those fruits from which he could remove and plant the seeds. He would eat apples but not strawberries, for instance. He refused to eat dairy products because his using milk might deprive a calf.

Stephen's pediatrician had told his parents that this was a case of *anorexia nervosa*, that Stephen's symptoms suggested schizophrenia, and that his recommendation was hospitalization and force-feeding with concomitant psychiatric treatment. The pediatrician based his recommendation on the medical literature concerning *anorexia nervosa*, in which it is considered that *anorexia nervosa* cannot be treated successfully in the home. The first report of a fatal case in 1895 suggests that the presence of the mother caused the downhill course.[11] And in two cases described in depth by Falstein, Feinstein, and Judas,[12] both patients regressed when they were returned home from the hospital, under the plan to continue therapy on an outpatient basis.

Because of the threat to life involved, the descriptions

available have been drawn largely from the study of children who have been hospitalized—that is, they have been separated from their natural ecology and placed in a new behavioral setting, one in which they are labeled seriously ill. Although some authors maintain that there is a consistent history of early struggles between children and parents over feeding and being fed as the battleground on which issues of autonomy and control have been fought,[18] there is no study of the *anorexia nervosa* patient within the family. As a result, the available literature presents the problem only from a strictly intrapsychic point of view.

This intrapsychic approach, which "zooms in" on the individual in isolation, recognizes that *anorexia nervosa* can occur as a symptomatic phase in divergent psychiatric disorders.[12]

> Eating may be equated with gratification, impregnation, intercourse, performance . . . growing . . . castrating, destroying, engulfing, killing, cannibalism. Food may symbolize the breast, the genitals, feces, poison, a parent, or a sibling.

The same authors emphasize the importance of the position of the adolescent in the family and internalized family conflict, but even here the field of observation is narrowed so that family conflicts are seen as somehow having moved inside the child. Where the starvation is considered an expression of hate and defiance against a mother who puts a great deal of emphasis on eating, this is considered to be the expression of an Oedipal conflict.

In the available literature, the boundaries of pathology are the child's skin. Concomitantly, the interventive techniques traditionally used with *anorexia nervosa* are directed only to the child. The interveners have no strategy other than separating the child from his natural contexts through hospitalization. Treatment in the hospital may be successful, but there is strong possibility of regression outside the hospital.[12]

If Stephen's pediatrician's recommendation had been followed, he would probably have been hospitalized after an individual interview. Prolonged treatment in the hospital would have followed. It would probably have included physiological measures such as the use of insulin and chlorpromazine,[11] individual psychotherapy, and perhaps behavior therapy.[8] Some therapy with the parents might have been included. This would mostly have concentrated on the mother, since the intrapsychic theory of *anorexia nervosa* postulates a symbiotic mother-child relationship.[12]

But Stephen's family refused to accept the pediatrician's recommendation. They felt that Stephen's problem must be a family problem, and they carefully reviewed city agencies until they found one which would take them into treatment as a family.

Since ecological psychiatry is concerned with the context for both diagnosis and treatment, we usually begin with exploring the child's most significant context, his family. Therefore, the first interview in Stephen's case was a family interview, not an individual interview.*

The observation of a child in his family presents different explanations of his behavior, depending on the observer's point of observation and the focus of his observation. The therapist in this situation is like a movie camera. He can zoom in and focus on an individual, as in the intrapsychically-oriented approach. But he can also widen his focus to include dyads, triads, the whole field, or any particular part of the field. (And he must realize that his presence changes the field he is observing, just as the fact that their picture is being taken causes people's behavior to change. Reciprocally, his behavior is in part regulated by the subjects of his observation.)

For the ecologically-oriented therapist it makes no sense to look at the child in isolation. Even when we zoom in on an individual, he is still seen as a member of a mutually regulatory group. Thus we could not see Stephen simply as a sick child. We saw him as an interacting unit of various relationships.

The relationship of Stephen and his father was the most salient interaction in the first interview. The father was the

---

* The therapists on this case are Salvador Minuchin, M.D., and Harry J. Aponte, A.C.S.W.

family member who was responding most to the presenting problem, Stephen's illness. Stephen's reaction to his father's very demanding control was a passive lack of response which clearly triggered increased effort on the father's part.

When we changed our focus to include the husband-wife dyad, we noticed a rather similar interaction between the spouses. The mother was very passive. She allowed her husband to dominate the family. Reciprocally, it was her very passivity that continually forced him to assume almost all of the executive power in the family.

When we broadened our focus to include Stephen, father and mother, we noticed the similarity of the two dyads and also recognized that the family's overwhelming concern for Stephen was covering up a problem in the spouse subunit. We could also hypothesize that Mrs. B's resentment of her husband was expressed in a covert encouragement of Stephen's rebellion against his father.

Broadening our focus to include the fourth member of the family, Matthew, thirteen, we realized that this was a family in which three members declared themselves healthy and the fourth, Stephen, accepted and furthered the label, "sick and weak." At the same time, there was another hidden three-one alliance. The mother and children were united in a passive coalition which triggered the father to control excessively, because the three saw the father as actually a very frail person who would collapse if any stand were taken against him. Therefore they protected him by maintaining an extraordinary passivity which promulgated the family myth that he was a very strong executive.

As a family group, the B's were low-key. They spoke softly and politely, with long pauses between interchanges. They did not evidence strong conflicts, and they were very obedient to the therapists. At points of stress, they took refuge in bantering and smiles.

Any description of a family system is necessarily static, given the nature of our descriptive language. Language is designed for sequence, so it is difficult to describe the continuous reciprocity of a systems intervention. The therapist reacting to, for instance, the mother's passivity must always keep in mind the way in which her passivity organizes the father to take control, which keeps her passive, and so on.

In spite of this sort of complication, the ecological point of view is very advantageous because it means that several levels of intervention are open. In this case, it was necessary to intervene promptly because of the threat to life represented by Stephen's refusal to eat.

After the first half of this first interview, which lasted two hours, we intervened at the total-family level by assigning a family task. This was Friday, and the family had already been scheduled for another clinic appointment on Monday. Over the weekend, the whole family was to eat only when Stephen would eat. The mother and father had to agree to this task, which they obediently did. Matthew was not given a vote; he had to go along if his parents did.

The selection of this particular task forced the family members to organize themselves around problems of regulation and control. A task is one way of creating a specific context within which the family members must interact. In this case we selected this particular task centering on control partly to test our hypothesis that Stephen's not eating was a reaction to a serious imbalance of power in the family, and partly to change the family's perception of the problem. We wanted to mobilize them around an issue that had some possibility of solution via family interaction—that is, control—instead of around a problem they could not solve, Stephen's *anorexia nervosa*.

At the same time, this task changed the family labels. For months they had been deadlocked in a focus on Stephen and his illness. Stephen was seen as weak, sick, and in need of protection. Stephen himself accepted and furthered the label of himself as somehow weak and victimized (a structure that hospitalization would have strengthened).

This task changed that label. The parents were redefined as powerless. Stephen was redefined as the family member in control. Matthew's not being given a vote defined him as a helpless victim of the family's inability to resolve the conflict.

This task also functioned as a further diagnostic device. By assigning a task which makes the family perform in ways it is not accustomed to, the therapist can test the family's flexibility of response. Making the family interact in a situation which cannot be met by their automatic responses tests the limits. Sometimes a task will do this by requiring that the family act in completely different ways. Other tasks, such as this one, intensify the tempo or impact of the natural family transactions.

The task performed a further function. We hoped to create crisis in the family by increasing the affective intensity of the situation. This technique of producing change by inducing crisis is based on our experience that a certain type of family, with rigid patterns of interacting, cannot change unless they are jolted out of their usual methods of interacting. The B family found it impossible to negotiate conflicts. Conflicts were always detoured or defused. We hoped that by creating a sharp conflict which could not be detoured or defused, we would force them to deal with the situation. This is an example of the use of iatrogenic crisis.[20,21]

When the mother and father agreed to follow Stephen's diet for the weekend, the therapists gave them their home phone numbers, with instructions to call them at any time during the weekend.*

The family had a miserable time, with hunger and resentment against Stephen building up. On Monday, during the session, we learned that on Sunday afternoon the father had shut himself in the garage, with Matthew watching, and turned on the car motor. As he later said, he did not want to commit suicide, but he did want Stephen to come and save him so Stephen would be taught a lesson. Matthew ran to get his

---

* When a therapist organizes a crisis situation in a family, he must insist that he is available at any time and will respond to any call. Mr. B's reaction points to the danger of this type of intervention. Whenever it is used, the family must be cautioned as to the possibility of ensuing crisis, and they must know the therapist is available.

mother, however, and the mother got the father out of the garage. In the session, Stephen said he had known his father was in the garage and what his father wanted of him. He had determined not to go to him, even if it meant his father's death.

With this task, then, several things were made clear. The father's method of control through guilt and Stephen's negative involvement with his father became unmistakably evident. The father's drastic reaction illustrated the extent to which a problem which had been conceptualized as Stephen's was built into the structure of the family.

In the session, the senior therapist attacked Stephen, his now obvious control of the family, and his value system of himself as the suffering protector of all living things. The therapist labeled Stephen as a despot who cared about all life except his own family, instead of as a victim of that family.

This relabelling shifted Stephen from the down position to the position of active controller of the family. Now, in the context of this structural change, the therapists again elected to intensify and explore the nature of the father-Stephen interaction. This time, both the mother and Matthew were labeled as powerless by the task assigned.

The father and Stephen were instructed to debate and decide, in the session, whether or not the family should continue to follow Stephen's diet. After a prolonged, no-decision struggle, the therapist intervened. He stated that a decision had been reached and that Stephen and his father had agreed that the whole family should return to a normal diet.

The therapists then indicated that they would be making a home visit and asked if they might come in two days. The therapists would eat with the family, and Stephen would plan the menu with his mother.

That evening the father phoned the senior therapist, saying that Stephen was refusing to eat dinner. Stephen maintained that he had only agreed that the rest of the family should stop following his diet; he intended to continue.

The therapist instructed the father to demand that Stephen honor the agreement but finally agree to let Stephen go on a full vegetarian diet, starting that moment. He explained to the father that in this way Stephen would experience himself as successful in negotiating with his father, and that the father would also experience a successful negotiation. About an hour later, the father called back to say that he had followed this strategy and Stephen had eaten a full vegetarian meal.

The initial crisis was solved. Stephen was now back on a full vegetarian diet, soon including dairy products; and in a month he attained a normal, if low, weight. The parents were instructed to disengage completely around the problem of eating, and soon no difficulty existed in this area.

This ended the case of *anorexia nervosa*. Among the many interventions available with an ecological approach, the therapists had elected to focus on the father-Stephen dyad and had organized a crisis in a context of heightened struggle for regulation and control. This manipulation had highlighted a specific, narrow problem in the family's interactional field. Because of the seriousness of the presenting problem, priority had to be given to the biological concern for survival.

Once the clinical picture moved from the acute illness of one family member to the chronic imbalance of the family, the therapists were free to broaden and change their foci. They made other home visits, sometimes driving out in response to a summons from the father to help negotiate another confrontation. Different family units were explored. There were separate interviews with the parents, Stephen was seen in individual interviews, there were sibling unit interviews, and we intervened at the level of peer group interaction by including Stephen in an adolescent group *via* an adolescent who joined the therapeutic team over the summer. In short, we used a variety of strategies, always keeping in mind the importance of specific contexts and the influence of transactions across systems.

For instance, two days after the second session we changed both the context of the interviews and the function of the therapists by making our first home visit, as arranged.

In the clinic sessions, the therapists had functioned as active manipulators of the field, introducing new situations and new rules, pushing the family, and observing the ways they responded to being pushed. In the family's home setting, the therapists functioned quite differently. They now were gathering data in the family's natural context, observing and becoming part of the family household as guests, affecting their data as little as they could in a visit lasting over five hours. They discovered many of the strengths of the family. Both boys acted as competent hosts, showing the therapists their rooms and the various articles in their rooms which reflected their many keen interests. The parents were also proud to present the positive aspects of their lives. They gathered a great deal of information about significant members of the extended family, which would later be useful in therapy.

Although the family's battles were no longer waged around Stephen's eating, they were still going on, of course. A new conflict area now arose; Stephen refused to talk. He kept silent for long periods of time, and when asked a question, often refused to answer. In this way the family's communications were now transacted in a way which was remarkably similar to that of the old eating conflict, though now in an area which was not life-threatening.

From an intrapsychic point of view, Stephen's dynamics could be interpreted in the same way, regardless of the change in symptomatology. But from an ecological point of view, a significant change had occurred. The family had moved away from its crippling focus on Stephen and his problems and had begun to understand the problem in their negotiation of conflicts. And the introduction of the therapists as significant members of the ecosystem meant a structural change in the form of negotiators who could help the family transact its area of confrontation.

The therapists also began interventions in the extrafamilial sphere. From an ecological framework, there are many behaviorial settings which can be utilized as pathways for the introduction of change.[2, 29] In work with adolescents, an obvious pathway is the adolescent peer group.

In general, the adolescent patient in therapy is expected to become free to move towards extrafamilial contacts by himself in the measure in which he improves in negotiating and developing autonomy in the family. But it seemed to the therapists that Stephen needed practical help in negotiating the complexities of adolescent society. As a member of a very enmeshed family, he had never made friends outside the family. He spent whole days at home, usually closeted in his bedroom, playing with his white rat. Occasionally the therapists were successful in persuading Stephen to go out, usually to the library, but this seemed to be the extent of his sorties outside the home.

In order to further one of their goals—increasing an age-appropriate autonomy in Stephen—the therapists decided to intervene at the interface between the family and the adolescent peer group. We introduced an adolescent therapist to the therapeutic team—a boy who would be Stephen's friend. This was accepted without difficulty by the family.

We looked for an adolescent who would have some of the nonjudgmental acceptance that some groups of "hippies" have. We chose a fifteen-year-old with hair longer than Stephen's, easy contact with adults, the ability to make friends easily, a capacity for benign, age-appropriate disengagement from his own family, and a thorough knowledge of the geography of teen-aged Philadelphia. He saw Stephen twice a week or so for four to six hours at times the boys arranged together. He introduced Stephen to a group of his friends, and Stephen became a silent and marginal group follower.

The adolescent therapist also served an interesting function for Stephen's parents. He attended the family sessions once a week, and the B's soon began to question him eagerly about his relationship with his family. They asked about his responsibilities, the extent of his autonomy, and so on. He served as a teacher for the entire family. The parents began to learn about "model family relationships" from an adolescent from a less enmeshed family; and at the same time, Stephen was carefully watching another adolescent dealing with adults, talking with them in respectful but independent fashion, and easily preserving his autonomy without the need for continuous confrontation.

Shortly after the adolescent therapist left for school in the fall, another intervention also designed to help Stephen achieve a more appropriate degree of separation from his family was effected.*

One result of our interventions had been an increase in Stephen's negative involvement with his family. He usually refused to talk, and in general, avoided contact. When there was contact, it was usually a clash.

The therapists decided to provide a finite period of separation from the family. We asked Stephen if he had any close friends he could visit. As he had not, the senior therapist invited him to his home for one school week.

I had already asked my own family if this would be acceptable to them; it was. Stephen was told that he was invited as a guest, not as a patient. He would have to discuss his diet with his hostess. He would have to arrange his transportation to school, using either public transportation or help from his parents to cover the long distance. It would be useful for him to meet my children, a daughter, twelve, and a son his age. He could observe my long-haired son's interactions with the family.

During the five-day visit, everyone in my family was on his best behavior as a family member. Our cohesion as a family increased. The experience was particularly important to my son, who shared his room with Stephen and felt primarily responsible for helping him adjust to the family.

Stephen showed remarkable ability to integrate himself with our family, in the face of all the stresses of adjusting to strangers. We tried very hard to predict his endurance, providing distance when he seemed to need isolation and inviting him to join in family situations when he seemed able to. Given this consideration, he did very well.

---

* This section was not included in the original paper read at the conference because this was a later intervention.

By the last day of the visit, Stephen was eager to return home. We held a session immediately following his return. In this session, he took the lead in presenting his family in a much more favorable light. His parents joined in this effort, working much harder than usual to present themselves as good parents.

This intervention produced in Stephen and his family a sense of competition between my family and their own. Laqueur has noticed this phenomenon in multiple family therapy.[16] When two families enter into competition, each increases the strength of their own boundaries and the effectiveness of their functioning in order to score points over the other family.

The B family was in treatment for about six months. There was no eating problem after the first four days of treatment, and the focus of the intervention shifted from Stephen to problems between the spouses, problems between the parents and the boys, and the individual problems of each member of the family. Therapy was successfully terminated.

Of the many interventions at many levels made in this family, the techniques discussed were highlighted because they illustrate some of the alternative methods of intervention which the ecological approach gives therapists.

This ecological approach brings its difficulties. One of them is the loss of therapeutic control consequent upon the broadening of the therapist's field. Because his areas of intervention are spread, his power in each area is diminished. Instead of the easily controllable dyadic setting, he is faced with many variables in many settings. This is an understandable source of the resistance to this model of therapy found in traditional child psychiatry.

If one takes this approach as a problem and a challenge to the field, it means that the child psychiatrist must change. He must build a large and flexible repertory of techniques for differentiated diagnoses and interventions. Then the very difficulties of this approach contain opportunities for the therapist to pick his area and method of intervention. If one pathway is blocked, there are many others.

REFERENCES

1. Ackerman, N. W.: *Treating the Troubled Family.* New York, Basic Books, 1966.
2. Auerswald, E. H.: Interdisciplinary vs. ecological approach. *Fam Process,* 7:202–215, 1968.
3. Bach, G. R., and Wyden, P.: *The Intimate Enemy: How to Fight Fair in Love and Marriage.* New York, Morrow, 1969.
4. Barker, R. G.: *Ecological Psychology: Concepts and Methods for Studying the Environment of Human Behavior.* Stanford, Stanford University Press, 1968.
5. Barker, R. G. (Ed.): *The Stream of Behavior.* New York, Appleton-Century Croft, 1963.
6. Barker, R. G., and Gump, P. V.: *Big School, Small School.* Stanford, Stanford University Press, 1964.
7. Bion, W. R.: *Experiences in Groups.* New York, Basic Books, 1959.
8. Blinder, B. J.; Stunkard, A. J.; Freeman, D., and Ringold, A. L.: Behavior therapy of anorexia nervosa: effectiveness of activity as a reinforcer of weight gain. Paper presented at the 124th Annual Meeting of the American Psychiatric Association, Boston, May, 1968.
9. Bowen, M: The family as the unit of study and treatment. *Amer J Orthopsychiat,* 31:40–60, 1961.
10. Bowen, M.: The use of family theory in clinical practice. *Compr Psychiat,* 7:345–374, 1967.
11. Crisp, A. H., and Roberts, F. J.: A case of anorexia nervosa in a male. *Postgrad Med J,* 38:350–353, 1962.
12. Falstein, E. I.; Feinstein, S. C., and Judas, I: Anorexia nervosa in the male child. *Amer J Orthopsychiat,* 26:751–772, 1956.
13. Haley, J. D.: *Strategies of Psychotherapy.* New York, Grune & Stratton, 1963.
14. Jackson, D. D., and Weakland, J. H.: Conjoint family therapy: some considerations on theory, technique and results. *Psychiatry,* 24:30–45, 1961.
15. Kramer, C. H.: Psychoanalytically oriented family therapy: Ten year evolution in a private child psychiatry practice. Family Institute of Chicago, Chicago, 1968.
16. Laqueur, H. P.: General systems theory and multiple family therapy. In Gray, W.; Duhl, F. J., and Rizzo, N. D. (Eds.): *General Systems Theory and Psychiatry.* Boston, Little Brown, pp. 409–434, 1969.
17. Leopold, R. L., and Duhl, L. J. (Eds.): *Mental Health and Urban Social Policy.* San Francisco, Jossey-Bass, 1968.

18. Lesser, L. I. *et al.*: Anorexia nervosa in children. *Amer J Orthopsychiat, 30*:572–580, 1960.
19. MacGregor, R. *et al.*: *Multiple Impact Therapy with Families.* New York, McGraw-Hill, 1964.
20. Minuchin, S.: Conflict resolution family therapy. *Psychiatry, 28*:278–286, 1965.
21. Minuchin, S.: Family therapy: technique or theory? In Masserman, J. (Ed.): *Science and Psychoanalysis.* New York, Grune & Stratton, 1969, vol. XIV, pp. 179–187.
22. Minuchin, S., and Barcai, A.: Therapeutically induced family crisis. In Masserman, J. (Ed.): *Science and Psychoanalysis.* New York, Grune & Stratton, 1969, vol. XIV, pp. 199–205.
23. Minuchin, S. *et al.*: *Families of the Slums: An Exploration of Their Structure and Treatment.* New York, Basic Books, 1967.
24. Perls, F. S.: *Gestalt Therapy Verbatim.* Lafayette, California, Real People Press, 1969.
25. Rice, K.: *The Enterprise and Its Environment.* London, Tavistock, 1963.
26. Riessman, F.; Cohen, J., and Pearl, A. (Eds.): *Mental Health of the Poor.* New York, The Free Press of Glencoe, 1964.
27. Satir, Virginia M.: *Conjoint Family Therapy: A Guide to Theory and Technique.* Palo Alto, Science and Behavior Books, 1964.
28. Shutz, W. C.: *Joy: Expanding Human Awareness.* New York, Grove Press, 1967.
29. Speck, R. V.: Psychotherapy and the social network of a schizophrenic family. *Fam Process, 6*:208–214, 1967.
30. Von Bertalanffy, L.: *General Systems Theory.* New York, George Braziller, 1969.
31. Watson, G. (Ed.): *Concepts for Social Change.* NEA, Washington, D. C., 1967.
32. Watzlawick, P.; Beavan, Janet H., and Jackson, D. D.: *Pragmatics of Human Communication: A Study of Interactional Patterns, Pathologies, and Paradoxes.* New York, Norton, 1967.
33. Whitaker, C. A.: Psychotherapy with couples. *Amer J Psychotherapy, 12*:18–23, 1958.
34. Wynne, L. C.: Some indications and contraindications for exploratory family therapy. In Boszormenyi-Nagy, I. and Framo, J. L. (Eds.): *Intensive Family Therapy.* New York, Harper and Row, 1965.
35. Zuk, G. H., and Boszormenyi-Nagi, I.: *Family Therapy and Disturbed Families.* Palo Alto, Science and Behavior Books, 1966.

Section IV

SOCIOLOGICAL PERSPECTIVES

Chapter Seven

Campus Psychiatry—the Batting Average of the Profession

HAROLD L. HODGKINSON

IN THIS PAPER I would like to consider a possible modification of the concept of batting average, moving away from a purely individualistic mode of cases "won" and "lost" toward a combination of interpersonal and institutional factors. As a sociologist and educational administrator, I would like to suggest some institutional criteria for your consideration. Simply to review the "cure rate" literature of Eysenck and many others would be futile, as you know this literature better than I. On the other hand, I am increasingly concerned in my research and travel for the *institutional* pathology I see on almost every campus. I do not buy the organismic model completely (a healthy organization is simply a bunch of healthy people), but the psychiatrist could be an extremely potent force in the interpersonal climate of an institution which affects everyone who is involved with the institution. There is ego *and* milieu. Both must be taken into account.

First, many administrators are able to develop effective communication networks on their campuses, but almost no one has developed an affective network whereby feelings and emotions can be transmitted to people who need to take them into account. (One exception to this rule is Dr. Elizabeth Sewall, the poetess who was in charge of Bensalem College, and never wrote memos to her staff but instead wrote poems to them.) For example, precious few college and university presidents use the dean of students as a source of information on how students think and feel. In fact, one of our interviews in the campus governance project reveals this comment from a president of a major university: "I don't trust student personnel professionals." Yet this kind of information has never been as important as it is today, and never have there been so many barriers between affect and people with administrative responsibility. At the moment I am afraid that many campus psychiatrists are not doing very well in this regard. Some have argued that it is a breach of confidentiality to make any report to the administration on what they are observing, but it seems to me that very valuable information about groups of students could be revealed without any loss of the confidential relationship whatsoever. At Bard College in New York State I had regular meetings with the psychiatrist, who could tell me what he knew about the drug scene on campus, the academic and social tensions students were feeling, and dormitory situations which seemed to him dangerous or frustrating.

Because the information was given to me in terms of *groups* of individuals, he never felt any violation of his obligation to protect the confidentiality of individuals. Putting this together with the other sources in our affective network (nurses, cooks, maid, buildings and grounds people, watchmen, etc.), a composite could be drawn from all these sources which was very helpful to me as an administrator trying to make the campus a better place for teaching and learning. Incidentally, the information from the psychiatrist was usually very much in agreement with the information provided by the other sources, indicating that they were reading the same conclusions from very different contexts. (The psychiatrist would, of course, have a much more sophisticated *explanation* for the phenomenon, but my interest was primarily in finding out what was going on, rather than having at that point a single explanation for the situation.)

Another very important role the psychiatrist could have included in his batting average is that of cultural broker, one who can provide nonevaluative feedback on a fairly objective basis which could help to reduce the factionalism which now runs rampant on American campuses. For example, in many teaching situations it is virtually impossible for the teacher really to find out what is happening, in a variety of ways, to his students. Ben Snyder at MIT has shown what can be done in this regard, by being a neutral broker, trying to communicate to faculty what they are actually doing for, and to, students.[4] One little example of his concerns a lecturer at MIT who developed a magnificent lecture, then memorized it so that the impression he gave the students was that he was just tossing the information off by free association, without notes. Rather than admiration, the effect produced in the students was one of deep and total desperation: "If that guy can do *that* without notes, I'd better give up." Through Snyder's feedback to the instructor a useful modification of approach was achieved and, conceivably, the instructor learned a little about his own ego needs as well as those of his students.

In similar fashion, disputes between students and administrators are often characterized by excessive escalation. On some campuses, there is no "back-stopping" at all, and problems which are nonexistent at nine in the morning emerge by noon as full-blown crises, whooshing from nowhere onto the president's desk without time for preparation. Tensions rise quickly, the level of argument declines, and moratoria are unthinkable to those involved in the fray. One primary characteristic of these adversary confrontations is that they tend to sweep everyone along to a high level of emotionalism, as everyone has staked out his "turf" which must be protected at all costs. The view of the problem becomes more and more shortsighted, less and less institutional.

This is not proposed as a panacea, but one with psychiatric skills could be extremely useful to an institution (and not just to the administration) in the development of what I have called precrisis management.[3] The first few minutes of confrontation are usually important in establishing what will follow. There is a very real possibility that at those crucial early stages a psychiatrist could act as a psychic buffer, keeping the level of aggression down, and the "cool" level high. As soon as ground rules can be agreed upon, and some sort of rationality established, the psychiatrist could phase himself out. (A digression on this point concerns the necessity for future administrators to get more training and experience in the nature of interpersonal processes. A psychiatrist could be of immense use in programs which train college and university administrators. Those things which drive people toward presidencies—aggression, social mobility, the exerting of power and influence, "leadership"—probably self-select individuals who have never been terribly concerned about, or interested in, the complexities of interpersonal process. Also, as "self-made men" they often may have real difficulty in isolating and assessing the reasons for their own behavior. I have no data on this point, but would bet that college presidents would find psychiatrists to be highly threatening. One might wish to investigate the problem of whether or not self-knowledge would lead to more effectiveness as an administrator.)

Psychiatric training programs for those working with students in colleges should attempt to reflect the total reality and diversity of campus life. Some of the recent research instruments in wide use to determine the quality of the campus environment, such as the CCI, CUES,* and the Institutional Functioning Scales, should be explained and illustrated. A rudimentary understanding of campus governance and of the examination and grading systems in common use would be extremely helpful. For the psychiatrist-to-be who is interested in asking his own questions, here are some which would be extremely important to his self-development in the field. What is the impact of pass-fail grading systems on psychiatric problems in students? Does the elimination of letter grades in the moving to a system of pass-fail have a significant impact on nervous and personality disorders in the student body? Why have the psychiatric and counseling services at such institutions as MIT, Wisconsin, Berkeley, and other major universities, virtually shut down during times of conflict on campus, with students saying they don't have time for their counselors

---

* College Characteristics Index, Collegiate Undergraduate Environmental Scales.

or psychiatrists as there are too many important things to do? On the other hand, as people in the counseling services get more involved in campus life one may see a reversal of this trend in which, as at MIT, involvement of clinical staff in student protests will be very high. What will this factor do to the quality of student protests? What is campus conflict like as a climate for learning? We know that students often feel a kind of epiphany, as was true with the students at Columbia who said that they felt closer to other human beings than they ever had in their life; but what do faculty learn in times of intense conflict? What do administrators learn? What is the impact of the size of an institution on the quality of interpersonal relationships that are possible within it? What can the psychiatrist do in this situation to increase the quality of interpersonal relationships?

One of the things which many juvenile or adolescent psychiatrists do is to recommend colleges to patients and their parents. How does a psychiatrist who cannot possibly devote the time to a full study of the collegiate scene make realistic and legitimate recommendations for college admission? Some student radicals have indicated that they feel that their strategy for change is quite like that of psychotherapy. They try primarily to take the implicit, hidden understandings, and make them as explicit and open as possible, on the assumption perhaps that this "therapy" will lead to a bettering of human relationships. The psychiatrist, of course, is interested in doing the same thing for an individual that some of the student radicals claim they are doing with groups—to find that which is masked and hidden from view and bring it out to full exposure. What are the implications of this position for the campus psychiatrist?

It is very clear that America at the present time is becoming a heavily age-graded society. Certain communities are made up entirely of young married couples with small children who are just beginning their occupational and social mobility patterns. As time goes on and success comes, one finds that these same individuals move out to different kinds of communities in which the predominant age pattern of the young consists of high school and perhaps college age people. From this one can move out to almost entirely adult communities, in which children are away at school; and then one moves to the retirement colonies in which there are no children whatsoever. In each type of community, because of the limitations on cost of housing, one finds the pattern of age segregation established rather strongly. This can be seen very commonly in major universities in which the "youth-ghetto" is easily seen. In these communities, such as Ann Arbor, Michigan, one can find that approximately 30 to 40 percent of the town's population will exist in very crowded, high density residences in which the residents have no control over the quality or expense of food, or rent, and have little say in the rules which govern the residence. This is not a slum, but is instead the population of students who make up between 30 and 40 percent of the Ann Arbor community and who may live in a density unmatched by any other sector of the community. In these communities, the language and vernacular of the ghetto is strong indeed, and perhaps appropriate as well.

On another institutional level, it is quite clear that American institutions of high education have become much more diverse in terms of their student populations. (In a national study of institutional change which the author has completed for the Carnegie Commission, 53% of the 1230 institutions in the sample reported increased racial diversity in the student body, while only 40% reported increased diversity of socioeconomic status of students. Institutions of higher education have thus become more open to races than they have to social classes.) [2] As higher education becomes continually less elitist and more populist, the problem of understanding subcultural differences by race, social class, and living area—rural-urban splits—will become increasingly important. One could argue that if America is to survive as a pluralistic nation, learning how to get along with others of diverse backgrounds will become perhaps our most important educational mission.

Many educational programs are being developed to help

train teachers and administrators from the third world generally, and to help those not from the third world to understand the particular educational problems created by ethnic differences. But I know of no such program designed to deal with similar *socioeconomic* differences. I wonder whether contemporary psychiatric training programs are helping the professional to deal more productively with the problems of race and social class as they can be found on today's college campus. Teaching and psychiatry are in a similar bind here—in both cases, the life styles, attitudes, and aspirations are unquestionably middle class. Just as the teacher favors the middle class student, so does the psychiatrist in a mental hospital favor the middle class patient, if the work of Leo Srole is correct.[5] I have seen the same teacher be relaxed and friendly, sitting on the desk in an atmosphere of easy informality with a class of middle class students, making jokes and tolerating a rather high noise level and much student disorder, then become rigid, highly structured, deadly serious and threatening when working with a lower class group just a few minutes later. Of course, the self-fulfilling prophecy works, the students perceive that the teacher expects trouble, and are happy to oblige. Similarly, the psychiatrist typically belongs to the middle class, and I would think would have some difficulties in working effectively with lower socioeconomic groups.

As I have read the material on social class and mental illness, I am struck by the report that the rate of psychopathology in lower SES areas is extremely high. In my work with people from these areas, it seems to me that in many of the environments in which they find themselves, that which appears to the observer as psychopathology may be a highly adaptive response to a virtually intolerable situation. Nowhere is this seen more clearly than it is in Claude Brown's *Manchild in the Promised Land*.[1] Similarly, when the ghetto child comes to campus, many of the problems of the clash of cultures are of a tremendously serious nature. Some of their responses may be considered pathological by white middle class teachers and student personnel workers, yet given the cultural imperatives, there are usually few other behavior patterns which could be substituted.

We are seeing just the tip of the iceberg if the populist movement continues in higher education. (There is little evidence to suggest that it might decline, and now some individuals are speaking not only of free higher education for all, but *compulsory* higher education—a very different thing.) Faculty are clearly going to have to consider not only compensatory admission, but the possibility of compensatory graduation. It may even be that the role of the psychiatrist, and what he considers effective practice will go through a similar revision as new types of students with different backgrounds and motivational structures come pouring through the gates of institutions of higher education. Adjustment and adaptation may mean very new things for these very new people. I wonder at times whether faculty, administrators and psychiatrists will be able to treat them as members of the human race, with respect (which they may not want), sincerity (which they will reject as Uncle Tom), and warmth (which they will see as co-optation). Whites are not used to being rejected by blacks, but it will be the name of the game for a time.

There is a retraining problem here of the first magnitude— many colleges are now giving white faculty time off to modify their courses to include the contributions of the blacks, from American history to modern poetry. What modifications will be necessary for those now engaged in psychiatry on the college campus?

For a number of years a pattern of middle class acquisition of lower class and ghetto cultural styles has been occurring, from dress, speech, and recreation, to music and dancing. These patterns are moving down to younger and younger age levels in the youth population. The drug scene, for example, has moved from the college years through the high school populations to become a present major problem in junior high schools in big cities. These new patterns do not make a virtue of impulse control, to put it mildly. Many of the students I now work with at Berkeley would have to be characterized as extremely well-adjusted ghetto residents, although many more conventional students and faculty brand them as being "disturbed." Psychiatry must come to grips with the problems of the "new student"—the black, brown, yellow and *white* underprivileged. Should they learn to suppress their rage, no matter how justified? If so, on what grounds? Should we try to convert them to middle class styles and perceptual patterns because of their superiority for getting ahead? The white upper-middle-class radicals (usually derogated by black militants for their childishness and lack of radical goals) are nevertheless fun for psychiatrists, like Keniston and Halleck, to study. I have seen few good studies by psychiatrists of lower class, or black, student activists. When a psychiatrist sets out to "help" these people, he must start looking at the word "help" in a new way. And what of the anarchist, who wants simply to blow the place apart? Can he be "adjusted"? Indeed, if one looks at the ethnicity of those in this lecture hall today, one is struck with the fact that the psychiatric profession itself seems to have recruited primarily white members of the middle class. One wonders what the consequences of this will be for the profession as it hopes or tries to expand its mission to other socioeconomic levels of the society.

And what of the exploding community colleges, opening at the rate of one a week? Are there functions for the psychiatrist in commuter, vocationally- and transfer-loaded two-year programs? I think the potential answer is yes.

Finally, let me state a personal conviction, based on research. There seems to be an identity crisis of some magnitude going on with many faculty and administrators on the campus today. The administrator characteristically has absolutely no one with whom he can discuss any of the problems which are eating him away. Even to admit the need to discuss these problems would be interpreted as a measure of inadequacy on the campus, yet the need is widespread, if not universal. We know of the increasing incidence of coronary disease in college presidents, but it is not usually known that some of the other adaptive responses to this unusual stress are also severe. The president has lost power on most campuses, yet he is still seen as the most powerful man there. This discrepancy in expectation and reality (particularly when the president *wants* to be powerful) can be enormously destructive. I have seen the wonderfully funny movie, *The President's Analyst*, and can see why few psychiatrists would want to get too much involved with the power group, even on a campus. But there might be times when the psychiatrist could shed his professional role for half an hour and become, for an administrator, a concerned and interested human being, perhaps the only person on campus who was neutral and safe. Chaplains are now occasionally playing this role.

Similarly, many faculty, particularly at the "on-the-make" institutions with their incessant pressure for more research and publication, are drinking more alcohol and enjoying it less. Sleeping pills and "exciters" are part of the normal diet. Nervous breakdowns are not unknown. The acquisition or denial of tenure is clearly a traumatic event in the lives of many junior faculty. The treatment they receive at the hands of their senior colleagues is often benevolent and enlightened, but it is also often handled as a rite of passage in which the young are made to feel pain inflicted by the elders and thus increase the elders' feeling of well-being and power. It also should be pointed out here that the teaching assistant is a person in intense role-conflict, half teacher, half student, often responsible for a great deal of the undergraduate instruction without being paid accordingly. If the Marxist analysis is useful at all in American higher education it probably could be seen with the full-time faculty as the bourgeoisie, and the teaching assistants as the proletariat.

Perhaps what is necessary is the creation of a new role—a person who can function with adults on the campus, yet knows youth culture as well. In our studies of campus governance one of the strongest impressions is that of a great paucity of interpersonal trust. The styles of collective negotiations, now becoming widely used in colleges and perhaps soon for universities, seem based on lack of trust, on the assumption that if people can codify everything (and some faculty work rules statements run to 60 pages or more) trust will not be necessary. Anyone who has tried can tell you that it is impossible to write everything down. Also leading from this style is the tendency to see people not as universes but as stereotypes (any student with a full beard is a radical, administrators are soulless bureaucrats, etc.). On today's factionalized campuses where shooting from the hip is an important style, stereotypic categorization will probably increase, as we can make a quicker response to a person if our response categories are limited to a few stereotypes.

This is, to put it mildly, a highly explosive state of affairs. I am not suggesting that the college psychiatrist step into the nearest phone booth, emerging as Superdoc, leaping into the battle to save the forces of good from the forces of evil. A psychiatrist is, after all, just another human being. But he is on the margins of the academic power struggle, and thus should be capable of encouraging trust and getting people to talk honestly to each other. His training will not equip him immediately for such a task. But suggested here is the creation of new roles, moving across the strata of academic, student personnel, and administrative positions as we now conceive them. Dr. Rosemary Park at UCLA now holds such a position, as do many others. College and university chaplains are beginning to move across the established lines of neutrality and are finding that there is much to be done. New team structures are emerging, even in psychiatry—there is a group in Chicago now providing psychiatric and psychological services for executives in major industrial corporations: Rohrer, Hibler, and Replogle.

Perhaps psychiatry has been concerned exclusively with pathology for too long a time. Some medical schools are now beginning the human anatomy course not with the study of the cadaver but with the pregnant woman—thus the shift from age, sickness, and infirmity to health, growth, and new life. The skills and perceptions of the psychiatrist are much too precious to be reserved for the consultation room alone. By dealing only with pathology, the college psychiatrist gets a rather distorted view of what is normal, also shutting himself off from faculty and administrative cultures.

The batting average of a profession, as opposed to that of the individual practitioner, must take into account the ability of the profession to provide new training programs to meet changing societal needs. One very clear example of this has been stated here in terms of the needs of American higher education. The campus psychiatrist who avoids the institutional questions may find that he will be of little use to students if the campus is shut down. The profession also might ponder these institutional questions, for some of the same reasons. Who is to deal with the anarchist, intent on destroying a campus? Were the leaders, Lenin, Mao, Che, "sick" men? What is the institution to say to the black militants? These are not easy questions, but we need all the help we can get, and often that help is coming from the margins of the power structure on campus, not from the center, where all initiative is being lost. To avoid these issues as a profession would be, in Auden's phrase, like lecturing on navigation while the ship is going down.

REFERENCES

1. Brown, Claude: *Manchild in the Promised Land.* New York, Macmillan, 1965.
2. Hodgkinson, H.: *Institutions in Transition.* Berkeley, California, Carnegie Commission, 1970.
3. Hodgkinson, H.: Student protest—An institutional and national profile. *Teachers College Record,* May, 1970.
4. Snyder, B.: Remarks from an informal discussion with the staff of the Center for Research and Development in Higher Education, Berkeley, California, October, 1969. (unpublished)
5. Srole, Leo *et al.*: *Mental Health in the Metropolis: The Midtown Manhattan Study.* New York, McGraw-Hill, 1962.

Chapter Eight

Adolescent Psychiatry:
A Sociological Perspective

PAUL R. DOMMERMUTH

THIS PAPER examines issues and problems within a relatively new segment of psychiatry—adolescent psychiatry— from a sociological frame of reference. It suggests that seg- menting and branching in a profession is continuous and involves redefining the division of labor within the profession through the development of new "unorthodox" missions, which attract new members, lead to new groupings and eventually to new social movements.[4]

This model—a practical method for dealing comparatively with the natural histories of professions—has the additional advantage of providing some guarantees against being led haphazardly into taking sides in internal battles within the practicing professions.[8]

Our involvement in this study stems from a dual tradition in sociology. First, we use a sociological social psychology with an emphasis on the perspectives that social actors develop and maintain within such delimited kinds of "worlds" as the work world of occupations and professions. Second, the tra- dition of the sociology of work developed by Park, Burgess and Hughes and their students at the University of Chicago since the 1920's focuses on the study of occupations as key compo- nents in the wider study of social order. This tradition views occupations as complex social institutions. As institutions they select people of varying competencies, often from diverse backgrounds, and organize them into social groups with ever- changing interests.[1,9]

The professions, as subclasses of occupations, "metabolize"

at differing rates. Social change within professions occurs as these various groups or segments pursue new lines of action which have diverse and at times conflicting impacts on the professions. In short, the professions are anything but monolithic in nature.

Developing these ideas requires understanding of the sources from which adolescent psychiatry evolved and the consequences that emerge from these changes for both the larger profession and the practitioners within the new segment. Before this discussion, however, we should explain how this study developed and what methods were used.

For the past ten years the author has been involved in studies of occupations and professions. During the first half of this period studies of various professional problems were conducted with engineers, industrial physicians and pharmacists, as well as beginning students in medicine, dentistry, public health and pharmacy. The last five years have been involved with a longitudinal study of professional socialization in psychiatry, internal medicine and biochemistry.

From this last study a variety of special research problems has developed.[2,3] In tracing the development of professional identities it became apparent that some trainees were specifically interested in following new career lines. In psychiatry this often took the form of choosing a new area such as community or adolescent psychiatry. In contrast to more traditional and well defined areas of subspecialization, both of these areas did not offer clearly demarcated career lines. To study this phenomenon in adolescent psychiatry we began—with the full support of the administrators of one training program in adolescent psychiatry—to collect data from many sources.

First we reviewed the literature through access to written reports of the local affiliates of the American Society of Adolescent Psychiatry, i.e. newsletters, notes on organizational meetings, summaries of periodic workshops, plus informal interviews with local and national leaders. This enabled us to chart the history of the organizational beginnings of adolescent psychiatry.

Although some of the local societies have been operating for almost ten years, the formal beginning of the national society goes back only to 1967. Since then we have observed the proceedings of two national meetings. While attending these meetings, a number of brief, informal interviews were conducted with leaders of local societies. At the meeting on training in Chicago a number of questionnaires were distributed with many of the issues discussed later in this report. Although the response was poor and would not allow references to be made about how local groups differ, there were enough replies to allow one to stake out the major alternatives on issues available to most of the organizational rank-and-file.

Finally, we had access to summaries of the papers delivered at the annual workshops of the Chicago society. These activities, coupled with attendance at the regularly scheduled meetings of the local Chicago society, enable us to feel confident that the main contours of adolescent psychiatry and its development are touched upon in this paper. In short, while the paper makes no claims for the verification of specific hypotheses about the nature of adolescent psychiatry or crucial issues within it, we hope to outline its primary characteristics and the directions in which it is apt to go. The next step would involve an in-depth study of key issues, e.g. board certification or changing membership criteria, the social and professional characteristics of the membership, and the manner in which these factors are related to such things as local differences or differential response patterns to any given issue.

THE NATURE OF ADOLESCENT PSYCHIATRY

The following discussion delineates adolescent psychiatry as an emerging segment within general psychiatry. It presents distinctive and "unorthodox" views and solutions to the dilemmas presented to society in general and the profession in particular by increasing numbers of troubled adolescents. The term "segment" refers to those groupings of psychiatrists throughout the country who are building and sharing both an organized professional identity and a set of common professional fates based on the burgeoning problems of today's adolescents.

With this conception of adolescent psychiatry as the base line for discussion, it is clear that we cannot begin with conventional, business-as-usual ideas about the nature of the field. This is true primarily because a fair portion of the data consists of the efforts of adolescent psychiatrists to separate themselves from general psychiatry and to identify new, and at times conflicting, conceptions of psychiatry. This pattern is fundamental for new segments within professions and usually takes place during the earliest stages of a segment's history. In short, new professional segments must develop a sense of mission if they are going to be successful.

The development of a sense of mission begins with discussions about the uniqueness of adolescence as a phase in the developmental continuum from childhood to adulthood. In proposing this emphasis, adolescence is described as a special period during which numerous unique biological, psychological and social tasks and skills are started, and hopefully accomplished. While little consensus seems to exist about the exact boundaries of this field, the literature clearly suggests that general age boundaries may be applied and that those within this age group constitute a coherent whole differing significantly from children or adults.

As spokesmen for the national organization often publicly assert, the adolescent exhibits a wide range of behaviors and it is incumbent upon psychiatrists to differentiate the "normal" signs of biosocial growth and personality development from the symptoms of psychopathology.[6]

The effective treatment of adolescents is based on an appreciation of these differences. While most readily agree that this period is one of emotional turmoil, this agreement is not evident when one turns to the issue of what constitutes proper treatment for those traumas which evolve into psychopathological states. Here several points of view are found, of which more will be said later.

A critical feature of any new segment's sense of mission

often is based on what may be termed as a *manpower emergency.* This usually takes the form of building a body of evidence which shows that the demands for services far exceeds the available supply. In adolescent psychiatry this case is built around a variety of unimpeachable sources, such as recent reports (1969) from the National Institute of Mental Health [5] which show an acute need for both traditional inpatient and outpatient services. Surveys of current service facilities show a steadily rising demand rate.

These figures are given increased significance when coupled with three additional sets of figures.[7] First, national population figures show that the pool from which potential patients come (the 10 to 17 age group) has doubled from 1958 to 1968. Second, checks of current services show that, in addition to rising demands, there are clear-cut signs that the gap between these demands and the projected manpower available to deal with them will, in fact, increase. Third, according to United States Public Health Service surveys, large numbers of private practitioners in psychiatry (about 64%) are already seeing adolescent patients without specific training in the special range of problems which most often manifest themselves in adolescence. These citations are used to show what those in adolescent psychiatry firmly believe—namely, that the time has long since passed when the nation can ignore the mental health problems of its adolescent population. The next step in tracing the development of a new segment involves showing how this mission indicates the need for new skills and special techniques for dealing with these problems.

TECHNIQUES FOR ADOLESCENT WORK

The most predictable action to follow a segment's development of its mission and its statement of the lack of manpower to cover this mission is the extension and revision of the theories, skills and techniques of its parent discipline to conform to this new mission. These changes in activities and methods have crucial implications for the formation of the new professional identity which eventually emerges for those committed to the segment. In fact these matters involve the very heart of the issue of professional change; new identities are formed as men cope with these changing conditions.

In some professions these steps involve radical revisions and often elicit labeling responses, which characterize those in the new segment as "heretical" or "unorthodox." Such responses come both from the "establishment" of the parent profession and from other professions with whom they share a work setting. If the changes called for are at sharp variance with the aims of these other groups, the typical rank-and-file member may often be caught in the cross fire of trying to follow these directives in resistant settings.

In the case of adolescent psychiatry the theoretical foundations clearly are anchored to the psychodynamic formulations of Freud and his followers. As far as one can tell few attempts to establish new theories, based on abandoning these foundations, appear. In part this is accounted for by the fact that this is currently the overwhelming theoretical persuasion of psychiatry. Another factor accounting for the lack of radical departures is the fact that a large number of the avant-garde, who have taken the lead in developing the area, are analytically oriented either in practice or by virtue of formal training. This appears to be true especially for those who come to the area from child psychiatry.

The absence of calls for these radical changes does not mean that there are not calls for, and efforts at, developing and extending present theoretical formulations, skills and techniques. The work of two leading figures, Peter Blos and Erik Erikson,* would fit this description.

The most consistent change called for is in the area of suggesting revisions in the techniques of psychotherapy which are cognizant of the peculiar nature of adolescence. The first change involves specific recognition of the fact that the initial stages of treatment are different from those of child and adult treatment. The conditions under which adolescents enter

---

* See Basic Reading List 5,11,12.

treatment, vis-a-vis parents and therapist, raise a series of questions about the potential effectiveness of treatment and the motivation of the adolescent, many of which may differ from the standard problems adults or children go through early in therapy.

A second change, usually couched in rhetorical terms, is the plea for flexibility in treating the adolescent. Implicit in the plea seem to be both the notion that adolescents require more flexibility than that accorded other patients and the criticism that some practitioners often have a tendency to mold their patients to fit their theories rather than the opposite. In this regard one spokesman made the point when he humorously remarked that consistent nondirective therapy with an adolescent makes about as much sense as nondirective surgery. This plea for flexibility also includes the use of various modes of therapy, family and group being the primary examples cited.

Another change cited in the literature centers around the need to establish clearly in the adolescent's mind the idea that the therapist is interested in his welfare and will actively work with him rather than become a detached "recorder" of his problems. Of course, the usual safeguards apply, but again the matter is one of emphasis.

All of the above changes are presented as examples of organizational ideology and rhetoric. The question with all of them involves not their presence or absence when compared with other fields but rather the manner in which they are emphasized and the consequences of this emphasis.

As new segments engage in these activities, which shape the growth of the area, they usually encounter resistances from both the "establishment" of their parent profession and from environing groups working on the same problems, often in the same settings. As noted above, the severity of these encounters may vary but the point to be stressed is that such clashes seem inevitable. Furthermore, it should be noted that adapting to these pressures almost always involves a major portion of the segment's early organizational efforts. These efforts often result in considerable compromise on the parts of the differing parties and not infrequently they result in considerable co-opting of the segment's plans for action.

Adolescent psychiatry encounters resistance primarily from the practitioners in child psychiatry and from those in general psychiatry who reject its special sense of mission and its concomitant claim of license and mandate to carry it out. From the child psychiatric group the differences revolve around its refusal to accept adolescent psychiatry's claim of the special differences between children and adolescents. These differences appear to have regional variations, since key figures in some of the local adolescent societies are, in fact, child psychiatrists.

Pressures from environing professions have not yet developed to any significant degree. When they develop they most likely will involve what may be termed the "narrow," psychiatric conception of the nature of adolescence. For example, the tendency of some psychiatrists to define adolescent problems almost exclusively in psychological terms with few attempts to broaden the number of factors accounting for them undoubtedly will lead to conflicts with other behavioral scientists. Essentially these differences result from the fact that most problem areas overlap the boundaries of two or more disciplines. This type of issue probably will lead to some battles about the restriction of memberships in local and national adolescent associations solely to psychiatrists.

THE NEED FOR COLLECTIVE ACTION

The primary problems for any new segment revolve around what is commonly viewed as the definition of a common set of problems and the need for public forums in which to discuss them. Early organizational attempts deal with defining these problems. Often these forums attract people with a wide range of backgrounds and interests. Thus, the early planning of a new organization involves much time spent on designing and developing a series of meetings which will attract new members who are willing to work. These activities provide the stuff from which a new segmental subculture emerges.

The various associations of a new segment quickly become involved in a variety of political battles on a number of fronts. Three typical examples are described since they seem to occur in a wide number of professional groups. First, new segments at the local level start to redefine institutional settings and work arrangements in them in a manner which takes their thinking and interests into account. Usually one finds a high proportion of those at the local level involved in these situations; this is not the case at the national level. Usually only a small number of the avant-garde or future-oriented care to, and are able to, get involved at the national level. Involvement is most appealing when it has immediate and personal payoffs.

Second, the new segment recognizes the need for a written forum controlled by the segment itself. The two basic methods used to meet this need are regional or local newsletters and a national journal. These official organs allow the group to promulgate their ideas to a wide audience and to respond to issues and charges other groups make. The political maneuvering involved in the establishment of a national journal often saps a young organization's vitality and the failures of such ventures stem from making these moves prematurely.

The third set of activities, vital for the group's success, are concerned with gaining new recruits in the form of incoming trainees in residency programs and those who wish to devote a major portion of their career to the work of the new field. Clearly these place demands on the segment for differentiated programs of education. Coupled with the issue of a manpower shortage is the crucial question of what to do with those in the field who have had either little training or experience in the field. Usually the founders of a new segment are self-trained; they use their experience as the basis for establishing their credentials. This approach seldom works for any length of time with a successful group and in short order the questions of credentials and certification become issues of paramount importance. This is usually the case because failure to provide manpower to handle the expanding market situation leads to much questioning about the ability of the segment to legitimate its claim of license and mandate for the area.

Problems of recruitment are more complicated than simply being in competition with others. They demand that specialized programs or rotations within well-established programs be established which project the imagery of the segment, the notion of a clear-cut segmental identification and finally, some reasonably identifiable career line. Such efforts are not likely to be successful unless the segment has access to, and preferably a measure of control of, residency training programs. For those who have completed training, the major form of education in an area is some form of continuing education, such as periodic workshops, intensive seminars or courses.

A related activity deals with the question of legitimation and official recognition from the parent profession, in this case, medicine in general and psychiatry in particular. The key issue at this juncture is whether the segment should press for recognition based on the traditional subspecialty patterns of board certification and all that it entails. Adolescent psychiatry is presently at this stage. The major meetings of the past two years have given specific attention to this topic. While all of the data are not yet in, it appears that the leadership of the national association is not in favor of adopting this model now.

The previous material represents a description of a segment in its early stages of development. Perhaps it would be worthwhile to comment briefly on the possibility of future developments in adolescent psychiatry. It appears that the basic issue proclaimed in its mission is valid. Crucial problems will involve the continued need to substantiate these claims.

As the segment grows, its members' interests and professional functions, the grist from which new identities are forged, will continue to proliferate and diversify. From these changes will come pressures which ultimately may lead to the emergence of new subgroups or segments within adolescent psychiatry. For example, the emphasis on clinical problems and their treatment may some day collide with the emphasis on scientific research on a somewhat wider range of problems. It is possible that such differences may lead to the emergence of two new segments: a practitioner segment based an applying current therapeutic approaches to these problems and a research segment less interested in these problems than in the broader range of factors involved in their etiology. To those with historical interest this pattern may be similar to earlier changes in psychiatry when the older somatically-oriented segment lost its dominant position to the newly emerging psychoanalytic approach.

In summary, this paper has focused on the stages through which new segments in a profession pass on their way to independent status. The case used here involved the relationship of a new segment in psychiatry, adolescent psychiatry. The evolution of the segment serves as a natural field lab in which to study the process of professional change in a substantive sense and in a more general sense, the process and problematics of social order and change. Many of the specific issues in adolescent psychiatry have been either ignored or touched upon in only a peripheral way. Studies of these topics involve systematic research of members of this segment; from these studies data may come which will clarify attitudes and make for enlightened and informed policy decisions.

REFERENCES

1. Bucher, Rue: Pathology: A study of social movements within a profession. *Social Problems, 10*:40–51, 1962.
2. Bucher, R.; Stelling, J., and Dommermuth, P.: Implications of prior socialization for residency programs in psychiatry. *Arch Gen Psychiat, 20*:395–402, 1969.
3. Bucher, R.; Stelling, J., and Dommermuth, P.: Differential prior socialization: A comparison of four professional training programs. *Social Forces, 48*:213–223, 1969.
4. Bucher, R., and Strauss, A.: Professions in process. *Amer J Sociol, 66*:325–334, 1961.
5. National Institute of Mental Health: *Patients in State and County Hospitals, 1967.* Public Health Service, 1969, No. 1921.
6. Offer, D.: *The Psychological World of the Teen-ager.* New York, Basic Books, 1969.

7. Rosen, B.; Kramer, M.; Redlick, R., and Willner, S.: *Utilization of Psychiatric Facilities by Children: Current Status, Trends and Implications.* NIMH, Public Health Service, 1969, No. 1869.
8. Schatzman, L., and Strauss, A.: A Sociology of Psychiatry. *Social Problems, 14*:3–16, 1966.
9. Smith, H: Contingencies of professional differentiation. *Amer J Sociol, 63*:410–414, 1958.

Section V

A SUMMING UP

Chapter Nine

Adolescent Psychiatry: An Overview

Roy R. Grinker, Sr.

I HAVE ENJOYED this conference very much. I myself am not involved in the treatment of adolescents, although I have studied what could be called healthy adolescents, so I will summarize this conference in my capacity of biased objectivity.

I am the administrator of an institute in which adolescent psychiatry has flourished. This conference has indicated that the people involved in this special field are dedicated physicians interested in treating patients and teaching younger professionals how to do it on the basis of their own experiences.

We have heard a good deal about the effects of treatment of adolescents on the growth of residents and supervisors as well as on the patients. I think that this should be documented, because as a general statement it doesn't really indicate how the triad mutually grows.

Each essayist told how this growth comes about in his own setting, and there is, of course, a great deal of variety, which there should be. If there were identical programs in each institution, we would make very little progress. I plead with you for more detailed statements instead of global, general statements, indeed, a frank discussion of the efficiency not only of the training program, but of the treatment results.

There has been some confusion in this meeting between adolescent psychiatry as ordinarily defined and psychiatry as applied to the college population of young adults. The young adult group needs to be viewed as a separate phase of the life-cycle. Timidly approaching career choices, we are seeing drop-out hippies who have renounced any further progress, and on the other hand, destructive protesters who are attempting to change the establishment into which they are about to enter. There are many gradations of reactions in-between.

The position of the psychiatrist as the educator of administrators and faculty, and as therapist of students, places him in a very difficult position. There are multiple demands and many restrictions placed on him. Nevertheless, we have heard the presentation of a magnificent program of social psychiatry at MIT. This is not simply a theoretical statement, but an actual description of operations, and this could well be a prototype for other institutions which attempt to deal with this difficult problem. The analogy to the military seems to me extremely interesting.

The question of countertransference versus the reality, which Dr. Kahne brought up in his discussion, is an extremely important problem, particularly within our current cultural and generation gap. Unfortunately, the explanation of countertransference processes is often a cheap way of explaining residents' and supervisors' failures. The therapist, whatever techniques he employs, must recognize that he is a real person *within* the social structure of his patients and this is particularly true with the adolescent and young adult.

The role of adolescents as teachers of psychiatry has been emphasized, but I find that there is little difference between adolescents and adults. We all learn from our patients whatever their age. Closed minds, characteristic of some elements of our psychiatric population, never learn.

I want to spend a few moments talking about Minuchin's very excellent statement of the ecological approach. This approach seems to me very important not only for adolescents and young adults but also for all of psychiatry. Linkages to the environment require understanding not only for those who are shifting from the family mesh into a peer group, but for all people who are moving in the social matrix.

I would suggest that we do not devise new meanings for words and statements and adopt them too readily. The ecological approach implies a bias toward a humanitarian approach which leaves out, I think, important aspects of the biological approach. I would rather talk about biopsychosocial approaches because there *are* biological processes which influence the capacity of individuals to learn and to adjust to group living.

Minuchin has moved toward a favorite field of mine since we published a book called, *Toward a Unified Theory of Human Behavior,* which is really the development of a systems theory. Some twenty-five years ago John Spiegel and I stole the word "transactions" from John Dewey and applied it to psychiatry,[2,4] and I can remember very well that our first presentation at the Chicago Psychoanalytic Society was followed by a deep, leaden silence. It is interesting to note that next spring the Chicago Psychoanalytic Society is going to have a workshop on general systems theory.

Minuchin has brought out that there are different laws and regulations in each system from the biological through the social, economic and cultural systems. Yet, these differences are grafted on some basic or isomorphic principles which apply to all systems.

The difficulty in thinking in transactional terms which is required if one is involved in field theory is serious. It requires three-dimensional thinking plus the concept of time, and this isn't easy. It can best be summarized by the term "unitary thinking."

Dr. Minuchin has done something which I think is extremely important because general systems theory will bog down as a global theory applicable to all systems unless it can be effective in operation, and Dr. Minuchin has brought clearly to our attention that one can legitimately and effectively operate within general systems theory.

Dr. Hendrickson has asserted that a repertoire of technics is necessary, that one should not devote oneself to one technic but give to people in trouble the benefit of the most appropriate therapy. That involves a serious task in the teaching program. Both Hendrickson and Gould believe that it requires a cadre of full-time teachers. Dr. Gould envisages a core curriculum of teaching and experience, in dyadic relationships. In this I believe the fundamental principles of relationships are established. The student learns the explicit language of his patient. He learns how to interpret meanings from the implicit language. He learns how to communicate in a reverberatory, cyclic manner, and he makes attempts to change the process of communication which will inevitably change the processes of thinking.

The question arises, as we are seeing the extension of our therapeutic endeavors from the dyadic relationship into groups, families and communities, whether this first experience hinders the development of these secondary processes. I have thought of the dyad as the basic experience from which one can extrapolate to larger groups. But I wonder now, after hearing the speakers today, whether the broader approaches are possible after a rigorous training in the two-person system of communication. The expectant magic of this basic training program is so great that it induces continuation in the same manner as the student has been taught, so great that it prevents him from becoming satisfactorily effective in larger groups.

Treatment is emphasized for what? Do we know the desired goals minus our own value system? Only a short time ago an early paper on normality was my Homoclite paper[3] which established the fashion of studying health and normality by psychiatrists, and you know Offer and Sabshin's book, *Normality*,[9] as well as Offer's book on normal adolescents.[8] We recognize that we cannot separate health and normality from illness, but that we have to speak of a health-illness system in which there are both healthy and/or normal components, according to our present values, and sick portions as parts of the total system, which is not static. It involves the total field with many functions. Included must be goal changing activities which are part of the process of learning and creativity.

Unfortunately, one of our distinguished psychologists called the student protesters at the University of Chicago paranoid. Other people talk about the basic violent characteristic of

American culture, and there are many other general state-ments. Maybe if we look at the problems from a different point of view, we may think of the adolescent problems as symptomatic of a revolutionary process moving from dualistic thinking, the individual versus society, to a unitary form of thinking in which there is unity in diversity and continuity in the change.

Where and how is adolescence if not determined by chro-nological age in the life cycle? It is a phase that cannot be defined by age. I think this is one of the tasks for the adolescent psychiatrist: to define the characteristics of adole-scents. As you heard in our discussions, there was some con-fusion as to whether we should treat people up to the age of twenty-one as adolescents. There is some confusion in the contrast between the college and the adolescent group, and whether there are really important ways in which one can discriminate adolescence as a phase in the life cycle. Where is it in the birth to death cycle? What are its interphases with other systems and with chronologically adjacent phases? To what degree is the life cycle fixed in adolescents, and how much movement toward differentiation and/or de-differentia-tion or regression is possible in the adolescent phase? Each phase has its characteristic internal processes, its specific stresses to which it is susceptible, and its capacities for defenses, coping and reconstitution. Adaptations, defense and coping are parts of a general process whose generic term is adaptation. With what does the adolescent cope and how?

Keniston[6] states this very well, although he neglects the increasing conformities required by our technological age. He says:

> . . . perhaps even more important, that industrial societies require of their citizens a high degree of individual autonomy, adaptability and self-direction. Industrial societies require rela-tively mobile and isolated nuclear families. The capacity to form and maintain such families requires, in turn, the ability to separate from one's family of orientation both psychologically and geographically.
>
> In a changing and complex industrial society, the individual

must deal with novel situations, temptations and opportunities both at work and off the job. He must be able to cope with novelty, to control himself in the absence of ritual and social pressure, to postpone immediate gratifications, to operate at a high level of symbolic thought, to enjoy and be gratified by relatively abstract and intangible operations.

Industrial societies such as ours, then, require high levels of adaptive functions of a sort that are difficult to guarantee if effective psychological development stops at the age of puberty.

The growing extension of adolescence provided larger and larger numbers of individuals with the opportunity to develop precisely the kind of technical and cognitive abilities, capacity for autonomous self-direction, and high level ego functions that are required by an advanced, industrial society.

This I think, is an important statement. One must think about it a great deal. Are the methods of coping and successes related to personality or life styles which have already been crystallized? This is a complex problem, and I think there are no current answers.

Regarding the evaluation of results, I think this is something that all therapists have shied away from, the notion of what are the results of psychotherapy, of psychoanalysis, of group therapy, family therapy, adolescent therapy, any form of therapy. We have avoided facing the issue.

I am sure Dr. Minuchin honestly described the work that he did with a family, and we all know of such anecdotes about the forms of therapy that we undertake. One family and one patient gives us the optimism that we can find a similar family and a similar patient, and the optimism necessary to cope with our own uncertainties and insecurity and to go ahead. Yet we need scientific evaluations of results.

Ernest Hartmann's paper[5] on the five-year follow-up study of adolescent inpatients is quite pessimistic, indicating that therapeutic intervention should be much earlier than adolescence, and forgetting that this is often when they come to us. Serious flaws in therapy are possible, but my analysis of his patients indicated that over half of them were borderline cases whose occupational adjustment after discharge was fairly good, but whose social adjustment was poor, as would be expected from the borderline case. I wish to correct Dr. Williams[10] for his use of the term "borderline schizophrenia." There is a borderline psychosis which is a behavioral term. People may be close to psychotic behavior or may have the tendency for psychotic behavior, but the borderline is a separate syndrome, and it is not related to schizophrenia and psychosis.

In our institute, a study of 161 adolescents hospitalized over the last ten years made by Garber and Polsky[1] is somewhat more optimistic, but still not good enough. Eighty-three were "making it." Twelve were drifters in and out of hospitals. Thirty had returned at least once to our hospital, and half of these are in state hospitals at the present time. Masterson[7] demonstrated increased depression and less acting-out at the termination of adolescence and in general clearer signs of serious illness as the adolescents grew older.

We need considerably more research along developmental lines. We need to know what we are treating and how, and what are the results, not as some child psychiatrists said, "We know what to do with disturbed children; the problem is how to teach it."

The excuses given are that there is so much time needed for service that little remains for research, and that it is not possible to do research without interference in the care of a particular patient. These are invalid objections. If adolescent psychiatry, and for that matter any part of psychiatry, is going to thrive it has to know at least partial answers to the questions, What are we treating and how, and what are the results? This requires the development of multiple models.

There was considerable irritation voiced at the notion that within the social system of MIT there was identification of the student with the aggressor teacher. I think this always happens, but I think there are identifications with others. Both in treatment of patients and in teaching of residents multiple models are important so that identification doesn't become skewed in one direction. Unless we have the capacity to furnish the residents these multiple models, we will find that they will be lavishly repetitive of the same kind of style practiced by a particular teacher.

Contact with research models takes time away from the therapeutic teacher. Supervision of people who are skilled in multiple aspects of research and training is necessary. This may be incorporated in the general residency training program, or may require an additional year. I hope that this doesn't indicate that I am advocating a specialization in adolescent psychiatry or a board for specialization.

In sum, I think we know too little about the problems, indeed, what they are, or in other words what are the questions. We spend too great a share of our time on doing something without knowing what we are doing. I think it is better to know at least a little more first, in order to do more later.

REFERENCES

1. Garber, B., and Polsky, R.: Follow-up study of hospitalized adolescents. *Arch Gen Psychiat*, 22:2, 179–188, 1970.
2. Grinker, Roy R., Sr. (Ed.): *Toward a Unified Theory of Human Behavior*. New York, Basic Books, 1956.
3. Grinker, Roy R., Sr.: Mentally healthy young males (Homoclites). *Arch Gen Psychiat*, 6:405–453, 1962.
4. Grinker, Roy R., Sr.: *Psychosomatic Research*. New York, W. W. Norton, 1953.
5. Hartmann, E. *et al.*: Adolescent in-patients: Five years later. *Sem Psychiat*, 1:60–78, 1969.
6. Keniston, K.: *The Uncommitted: Alienated Youth in American Society*. New York, Harcourt, Brace and World, 1960.
7. Masterson, James F.: *The Psychiatric Dilemma of Adolescence*. Boston, Little Brown, 1967.
8. Offer, Daniel: *The Psychological World of the Teen-ager*. New York, Basic Books, 1969.
9. Offer, Daniel, and Sabshin, Melvin: *Normality: Theoretical and Clinical Concepts of Mental Health*. New York, Basic Books, 1966.
10. Williams, F. S.: Discussant. Conference on Training in Adolescent Psychiatry. Chicago, 1969.

APPENDIX

A

Position Statement on
Training in Adolescent Psychiatry
American Society for Adolescent Psychiatry

WILLIAM A. SCHONFELD

THE NEED FOR MORE services and trained manpower to deal with the psychiatric needs of adolescents is clear. The National Institute of Mental Health reports that more than one-fourth of all psychiatric clinic patients are adolescents. The recent increase in the inpatient adolescent population is overwhelming, with a 500 percent increase among boys and 150 percent increase among girls in the past fifteen years. It is urgent that additional psychiatrists receive training in how to meet these needs.

The American Society for Adolescent Psychiatry recommends that training in adolescent psychiatry be made available within the present residency structure as authorized by the Joint Residency Review Council of the American Board of Psychiatry and Neurology and the American Medical Association's Council of Medical Education. Five training levels are delineated: the psychiatry resident, the resident with a special interest in adolescence, the fellow in child psychiatry, the career adolescent psychiatrist and the psychiatrist in practice.

All psychiatric residents should have supervised training and experience with adolescents during their three years of training. Trainees who wish more extensive involvement in this area should have the opportunity to take, as their third year of residency, an elective in adolescent psychiatry. Child psychiatry fellows with an interest in adolescents should have the same opportunity for a full year's elective in adolescent psychiatry; this, with a year's additional training in child psychiatry, would satisfy the residency requirements for certification in the subspecialty of child psychiatry. Those interested in college psychiatry should be offered the opportunity to study at a college psychiatric training facility. The existing one and two year fellowships in adolescent psychiatry currently being funded by the National Institute of Mental Health on the fourth and fifth year levels should be continued for those who plan to become career adolescent psychiatrists.

Competence in diagnosis and treatment is the core aim of general psychiatric training. The technical problems of working with adolescents require knowledge of the physical, cognitive and affective aspects of growth and development, the dynamics of family involvement and interaction, the significance of peers, the impact of school and recreational activities and the total spectrum of adolescent behavior.

The resident must learn, under supervision, the techniques of individual interviewing and psychotherapy with adolescents and with their parents, psychopharmacotherapy, group therapy, conjoint family therapy and crisis intervention techniques. He must be informed about various sociotherapeutic approaches, community psychiatry, the varied concepts of educational disabilities and their remedies, and psychological tests and their significance. The concepts of milieu therapy must become familiar.

He must learn how to collaborate effectively as a teacher and consultant with all the disciplines working with youth.

The college psychiatrist needs awareness of the sociological structure of the total college community. He may be working with administrative, faculty and dormitory staffs as well as the students.

Involvement in specific research projects relating to adolescents is to be encouraged.

A combination of adolescent inpatient and outpatient services provides the basic components of an effective training facility. In residency programs which lack these services the trainees should be rotated through affiliate organizations which can provide them. These could include hospitals, clinics, residential treatment centers or schools, day hospitals, group homes, halfway houses or residence clubs for adolescents, and the psychiatric services of courts and probation departments. Additional opportunities exist in the adolescent clinics designed to care for general medical needs. Schools, both public and private, the emergency services of general hospitals, aftercare clinics, neighborhood health centers, drug abuse clinics, and special settings such as homes for unwed mothers also provide valuable opportunities for study.

What is required is actual and extensive experience with adolescents, under the supervision of psychiatrists trained and experienced in working with the age group.

The American Psychiatric Association's Task Force on Continued Education has stressed the need for continued education. The Task Force may recommend that each District Branch undertake to give refresher courses to its members. Adolescent psychiatry may be one area requiring such instruction. The local affiliate society of the American Society for Adolescent Psychiatry could foster such clinical seminars in collaboration with the District Branch.

RECOMMENDATIONS

The purpose of the American Society for Adolescent Psychiatry's Position Statement on Training in Adolescent Psychiatry is to suggest the means by which training in adolescent psychiatry could be implemented into graduate psychiatric training. These recommendations will be submitted to the American Psychiatric Association and the American Board of Psychiatry and Neurology for their support, review and reactions.

The responsibility for establishing what the required residency training should be lies with the Joint Residency Review Council of the American Board of Psychiatry and Neurology and the American Medical Association's Council of Medical

Education. It is to this Council that these recommendations are directed:

1. There is no need for a special Certifying Board in Adolescent Psychiatry. Psychiatrists with special interest in adolescents should come from both general psychiatry and child psychiatry.

2. There is an urgent need to include training in adolescent psychiatry for all psychiatric residents:

    A. The Council should strongly recommend to the approved Residency Training Centers that they give all trainees supervised experience with adolescents during the three years of the General Psychiatric Residency in those clinical facilities for training available in the community in which the training center is located. No resident is expected to involve himself with all the facilities for training, but all residents should be involved with some of the facilities.

    B. The Council should "urge" the training centers to broaden their existing programs to cover adolescents by including questions on adolescent psychiatry on both the written and oral examinations of the American Board of Psychiatry and Neurology in general psychiatry.

3. Opportunities should be provided for special training in adolescent psychiatry for all residents who desire this in their third year of psychiatric residency.

4. The third year could also serve as the first year of the Child Psychiatry Residency for those who wish to go on to child psychiatry.

5. The National Institute of Mental Health should also be encouraged to support more special career adolescent psychiatric fellowship training programs.

6. Special training programs for college psychiatry should be available.

7. The affiliated societies of the American Society for

Adolescent Psychiatry should make available to the District Branches of the American Psychiatric Association and to hospitals requesting assistance, personnel to organize training seminars in adolescent psychiatry for extended psychiatric education of the practicing psychiatrist and/or staff psychiatrist, both as long range, part-time and concentrated full-time programs.

B

Basic Reading List on Adolescence

1. Aichorn, A.: *Wayward Youth.* New York, Viking, 1948.
2. Ausubel, D. P.: *Theory and Problems of Adolescent Development.* New York, Grune & Stratton, 1954.
3. Ames, L. B.; Metraux, R. W., and Walker, R. N.: *Adolescent Rorschach Responses.* New York, Hoeber-Harper, 1959.
4. Becket, P. G. S.: *Adolescents Out of Step.* Detroit, Wayne University, 1967.
5. Blos, P.: *On Adolescence.* New York, Free Press, 1962.
6. Cohen, Albert K.: *Delinquent Boys: The Culture of the Gang.* Glencoe, Illinois, Free Press, 1955.
7. Coleman, J. L.: *The Adolescent Society.* Glencoe, Illinois, Free Press, 1961.
8. Deutsch, H.: *Selected Problems of Adolescence.* New York, International Universities Press, 1967.
9. Douvan, E., and Adelson, J.: *The Adolescent Experience.* New York, Wiley, 1966.
10. Easson, W.: *The Severely Disturbed Adolescent.* New York, International Universities Press, 1969.
11. Erikson, E. H.: *Youth: Identity and Crisis.* New York, W. W. Norton, 1968.
12. Erikson, E. H. (Ed.): Youth: Change and challenge. *Daedalus,* Winter, 1962.
13. Farnsworth, D. L.: *Psychiatry, Education and The Young Adult.* Springfield, Thomas, 1966.
14. Feuer, L. S.: *The Conflict of Generations.* New York and London, Basic Books, 1969.
15. Freud, A.: *The Ego and Mechanisms of Defense.* New York, International Universities Press, 1946.
16. Friedenberg, E. Z.: *The Vanishing Adolescent.* Boston, Beacon, 1959.
17. Friedenberg, E. Z.: *Coming of Age in America.* New York, Random House, 1965.
18. Glueck, S., and Glueck, E.: *Delinquents & Non-delinquents in Perspective.* Cambridge, Harvard University Press, 1968.

19. Hartmann, E. *et al.*: *Adolescents in a Mental Hospital.* New York, Grune & Stratton, 1968.
20. Hall, J. Stanley: *Adolescence (2 Vols.).* New York, Appleton, 1916.
21. Heath, D. H.: *Growing Up in College.* San Francisco, Jossey-Bass, 1968.
22. Holmes, D.: *Psychotherapy With Adolescents.* Boston, Little Brown, 1966.
23. Hollingshead, A. B.: *Elmtown Youth.* New York, Wiley, 1949.
24. Josselyn, I.: *The Adolescent and his World.* Family Service Association of America, 1952.
25. Kaplan, G., and Lebovici, S. (Eds.): *Adolescence: Psychosocial Perspective.* New York and London, Basic Books, 1968.
26. Keniston, K.: *The Uncommitted.* New York, Harcourt, Brace & World, 1965.
27. Kiel, N.: *The Universal Experience of Adolescence.* New York, International Universities Press, 1964.
28. Kiel, N.: *The Adolescent Through Fiction.* New York, International Universities Press, 1959.
29. Lorand, S., and Schneer, H. I. (Eds.): *Adolescents.* New York, Hoeber-Harper, 1961.
30. Masterson, J. F.: *The Psychiatric Dilemma of Adolescence.* Boston, Little Brown, 1967.
31. Mead, M.: *Growing Up in Samoa.* New York, New American Library, 1928.
32. Miller, A.; Giovacchini, P., and Feinstein, S. C. (Eds.): *Annals of Adolescent Psychiatry.* New York and London, Basic Books, 1971.
33. Muss, R.: *Theories of Adolescence.* New York, Random House, 1962.
34. Offer, D.: *The Psychological World of the Teen-ager.* New York and London, Basic Books, 1969.
35. Pearson, G. H.: *Adolescents and the Conflict of Generations.* New York, W. W. Norton, 1958.
36. Sanford, N: *The American College.* New York, Wiley, 1962.
37. Seidman, J. M. (Ed.): *The Adolescent.* New York, Holt, Rinehart and Winston, 1965.
38. Slavson, S. R.: *Reclaiming the Delinquent.* Glencoe, Illinois, Free Press, 1965.
39. Symonds, P. M.: *Adolescent Fantasy.* New York, Columbia University, 1949.
40. Thrasher, F. M.: *The Gang.* University of Chicago, 1936.
41. Task Force Report: *Juvenile Delinquency and Youth Crime.* The

President's Commission on Law Enforcement and Administration of Justice, Washington D. C., 1967.
42. Weiner, I. B.: *Psychological Disturbance in Adolescence.* New York, Wiley, 1970.
43. Wittenberg, R.: *Post Adolescence: Theoretical and Clinical Aspects of Psychoanalytic Therapy.* New York, Grune & Stratton, 1968.

INDEX